A selection (

G000155352

Best Inns & ___ ___
in the South East

Compiled by: Gordon Dunkerley
                    Colin Whiteley
                    John Wilson

Edited by: James Lawrence

CONTENTS

Published by

Bracken Publishing
Bracken House, 199a Holt Road
Cromer, Norfolk NR 27 9JN

ISBN 1 871614 08 2

Printed by Broadgate Printers, Aylsham, Norfolk.

July 1991

Introduction

"The Garden of England", a phrase commonly used with regard to Kent, is perhaps equally apposite in respect of the other counties of Sussex, Hampshire and Surrey. Well manicured and cultivated as a garden should be, the region grows much of the country's food produce, and the endless acres of orchards are a spectacular sight when in the full blossom of spring. More relevant, perhaps, it is also the leading hop growing area, so naturally some very fine beers are brewed.

Historically, the region is of crucial importance. The many would-be conquerors who have cast a covetous eye to our island have always first to address themselves to this little corner. Anyone who has stood on the cliffs of Dover on a clear day will know how perilously close we are to an often troubled continent, but our 'moat' has been just wide enough to save us, at least since 1066. The sight of those white cliffs appearing (or disappearing) over the horizon has evoked many a lump in the throat.

The channel tunnel will end our 'splendid isolation', and no doubt have a considerable effect on Kent, especially. The South East is already the most 'developed' and densely populated part of the country. To a degree, it is a dormitory to London, and the capital has swallowed much of Surrey and parts of Kent. But for all this, the newcomer will be surprised to discover a green, fragrant countryside, peaceful little villages at the end of lush, leafy lanes, and ofcourse the ancient, unspoilt Downs.

Since before the days of Chaucer, travellers have sought refreshment in the many wayside inns, in which the counties are still well blessed. And what could more English than the country pub? Ask any foreign visitor what he or she most likes about England and the answer will almost certainly include "your pubs". They are a continuing thread through our social history, and one feels that so long as they are still there, things aren't so bad.

But there have been changes in recent years: the intrusion of noisy juke boxes and games machines is a blight, but standards of food and beer have improved dramatically. The last two years have been turbulent for the trade, to say the least. Many tenants are quitting in the face of huge rent increases, and freeholders are unable to sell since the collapse of the property market. The consequent uncertainty has made compiling a guide such as this very difficult. Numerous pubs could not be included because it was likely that the publican would be gone by time of publication, or shortly thereafter.

Nevertheless, we are pleased to present this first edition, intended to point both locals and visitors to some of the better inns and pubs, following the same formula which has proved so successful for our guides to other regions. Each one is revised, updated and improved every year, and readers' comments about any establishment, whether featured or not, are most helpful in this endeavour.

I hope you will find this guide useful, and should it lead you to discover a good inn or pub, please tell the proprietor!

Important

Please note:-

1. *Dishes quoted from menus are examples only, and not necessarily available at all times.*

2. *The listing of brewers' beers and lagers does not mean that their full range is necessarily available.*

3. *Prices, where quoted, may alter during the currency of this guide.*

4. *Every effort is made to ensure accuracy, but inevitably circumstances alter and errors and omissions occur. Therefore the publisher cannot accept liability for any consequences arising therefrom.*

5. *This is a selection: it is not claimed that all the best inns and pubs are featured.*

6. *Your comments about any establishment, favourable or not, are particularly welcome. Correspondents who especially impress the editor will receive a complimentary copy of the next edition.*

7. *Special note to publicans: if your house is not included, please do not be offended! The area covered is large, and time limited. If you serve good food in pleasant surrounds, please write and we will visit you.*

FURTHER COPIES OF THIS OR OUR OTHER GUIDES MAY BE OBTAINED BY WRITING TO:-

> Bracken Publishing
> Bracken House
> 199a Holt Road
> Cromer
> Norfolk NR27 9JN

Other guides:-

> Eastern Counties
> Eastern Counties Hotels & Restaurants
> Cotswolds, Thames Valley & Chilterns
> Midlands
> West Country

Enclose payment of £3.50 per copy, to include postage etc. No orders will be accepted without prior payment, other than from book retailers.

OTHERS IN THIS SERIES

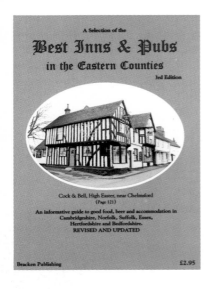

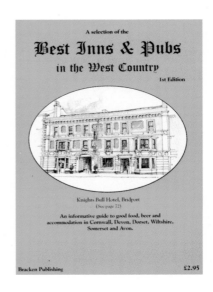

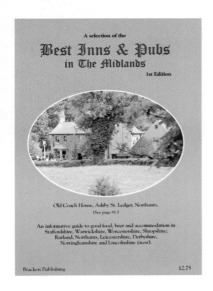

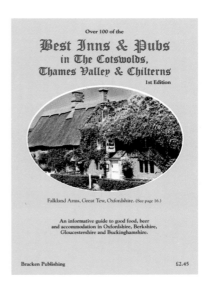

Also published: *Best Hotels and Restaurants in the Eastern Counties*.

Available in most bookshops and some pubs within area, or by writing to Bracken Publishing, enclosing payment of £3.50 (to include postage).

KENT

Scotney Castle, Lamberhurst

THE BROWN TROUT

The Down, Lamberhurst.   Tel. (0892) 890312

            Location: On B2169, almost opposite Scotney Castle.
    Credit cards: Access, Visa.
             Bitters: Flowers, Marston's Pedigree.
              Lagers: Heineken, Heineken Export, Stella Artois.

Examples of bar/restaurant meals (lunch & evening, 7 days): *venison in red wine, trout with walnut & celery, chicken Kiev, steaks, veal a la creme, skate, lobster, crab, fresh plaice, mussels, oysters, ploughman's, sandwiches, daily specials. Trad. Sun. roasts.*

This exceptionally pretty pub is also one of the most popular in the area, so be advised to book well ahead if planning to dine on a Saturday evening. The reason is not hard to see; a varied and extensive choice of good food, served in generous portions, yet reasonably priced. It's also a very pleasant spot to just quietly sup ale. Cottage origins are unmistakable, with a large inglenook and beams and lattices bedecked with brasses and prints (mostly depicting trout fishing). The noble fish naturally appears on the menu, and may be enjoyed in either bar or restaurant. On your way to the latter you may like to view a very fine tropical aquarium. The atmosphere is relaxed, the staff helpful, and landlord Jo Stringer permits children - the garden has swings and trampoline. Superb example of oast houses just opposite.

THE PRINCE OF WALES

High Street, Cranbrook.   Tel. (0580) 713058

Location: Near village centre.
Credit cards: Not accepted.
Bitters: Harveys, guests. Regular beer festivals.
Lagers: Becks, Carlsberg, Tennants, Tennants Extra.

Examples of bar meals (lunch & evening, 7 days): *homemade lasagne, chilli, cauliflower cheese, homemade pizzas, filled jacket potatoes, burgers, toasted sandwiches, daily specials.*

Cranbrook is one of Kent's prettiest villages (or small town, perhaps), and this lively, sporting pub is something of a focal point of village social life. Over 300 years old, it was once known as The Limes Hotel. Friendly, unspoilt and unpretentious, it has its own rugby team and hosts a beer festival four or five times per year. Though finding a regular place in good beer guides, not only traditional bitters are taken seriously - a range of special imported lagers is stocked. Bar food is homecooked (including pizzas prepared to order), nutritious and reasonably priced, and one may partake in either of the bars or small dining area. A games room has a pool table and doubles for functions, and there is a children's room. The sunny front garden has tables and chairs. Vivienne, John and Sue are your affable hosts.

THE WILD DUCK

Marden Thorn, Marden.   Tel. (0622) 831340
>   Location: East of village.
>   Credit cards: Access, Visa.
>   Bitters: Fremlins, Wadworth 6X, Larkins.
>   Lagers: Fosters, Kronenbourg.

Examples of bar meals (lunch & evening, except Sun & Mon evenings): *all day breakfast, Mexican specialities, fish 'n' chips, lasagne, steaks, scampi, salads, ploughman's, sandwiches, pie of the day.*
Examples of restaurant meals (Tues - Sat evening, plus Sun lunch): *wild duck liver pate, devilled kidneys, salmon in wine & lobster sauce, roast lamb, steaks, wild duck in orange or black cherry sauce, beef stroganoff, scampi thermidor, almond trout, vegetarian dishes.* NB Pub is open 11am - 11pm, and there are plans to serve food lunch & evening every day.

This much esteemed old pub (age uncertain) stands secluded amongst orchards and meadows, and what better way to conclude a spin through leafy lanes than with a good pint and homecooked food in warm, convivial surrounds? Like so many of the better concerns, this one is family run; Eric and Hilary Watson have put in over three years here. Their new restaurant (children welcome) is tastefully decorated, and enjoys a pleasant aspect over the patio (occasional barbecues) and garden (with play equipment). It doubles as a function room, suitable for a wedding reception, and a marquee is available if required. There's one oak beamed bar and a restaurant bar, where occasional special evenings are arranged. Super ladies' loo!

THE KING'S ARMS

1 High Street, Headcorn.   Tel. (0622) 890216

Location:	Village centre.
Credit cards:	Not accepted.
Accommodation:	2 doubles, 1 twin. Central heating, tea & coffee. £34 per room.
Bitters:	Fremlins, Flowers IPA & Original, Harveys.
Lagers:	Stella Artois, Heineken, Heineken Export.

Examples of bar/restaurant meals (lunch & evening, 7 days): *fresh dressed crab, shell-on prawns in garlic, salmon steak, cod, grilled fresh sardines, home-baked gammon, beef stroganoff, fresh plaice with prawn &cheese sauce, steak & kidney pie. Trad. Sun. roasts (booking advised).*

Jazz lovers should keep their Friday evenings free, for that is when many of the top names in the business perform live at this super venue. Solo or duo artists play every Wednesday evening in the main bar, mostly popular music from the 50s, 60s and 70s. Once the haunt of smugglers, this attractive 16th century inn is celebrated not only for exciting musical soirees, but also for outstanding fresh and home prepared food; so much so, in fact, that it was necessary to extend the restaurant to almost double its former size. The menu varies daily, with fresh fish always strongly featured, including sardines, a house speciality. Graham and Ann Moore have earned their success over 20 years here, which is quite exceptional in a trade becoming increasingly transient. They welcome children, and have a nice garden where barbecues are held in summer. Car park. Beautiful Leeds Castle nearby.

THE ROSE & CROWN

Stone Street, nr Seal, Sevenoaks.   Tel. (0732) 810233

       Location: Village centre, between Seal and Ivy Hatch.
  Credit cards: Not accepted.
        Bitters: Fremlins, Flowers, Harveys.
        Lagers: Stella Artois, Heineken.

Examples of bar/restaurant meals (lunch & evening, 7 days. Limited menu Mondays): *seasonal specialities (incl. game), smoked fish platter (noted), crab soup, skate, plaice, scampi, chicken chasseur, duck al'orange, guinea fowl, veal kidneys giannini, mussels, entrecote pizzaiola, steaks, daily specials. Homemade desserts.*

Booking is advised every evening - good food at reasonable prices will always draw them in. Naturally, it is fresh and homecooked, and varies according to season; expect to find hare, venison etc in winter, and fresh shellfish in summer. The menu blends English and continental cuisine, with perhaps an Italian accent - Luigi and Debbie Carugati are the proprietors. After recent refurbishment (public bar), the exposed timbers and stone walls of this venerable old building now reverbrate a liitle to the strains of live jazz evenings, but essentially this is a quiet country pub, undisturbed by juke boxes or indoor games. Children are welcome, ofcourse, and will enjoy the barbecues in the large sunny garden. Apple orchards supply a pleasant aspect to the front, and Ightham Mote is a nearby attraction. Large car park.

THE VIGO INN

Fairseat, nr Sevenoaks.   Tel. (0732) 822547

Location:	On A227, 2 miles off M20.
Credit cards:	Not accepted.
Bitters:	Vigo Best, Goachers Dark, Youngs, Harveys, guest.
Lagers:	Youngs London, Carlsberg Export.

Variety of filled rolls always available.

We all know of pubs so taken over by food that one feels that drinkers are not really welcome, or at best just tolerated. But here is a truly traditional country inn, where customers make their own conversation over a pint of the very best cask conditioned beer, without music of any kind, nor gamimg machines to intrude. Food is limited to light snacks, and even tobacco products and matches are not sold. There is diversion in the form of 'Dadlums', an old game of skittles, of which this is thought to be the only remaining original. The name 'Vigo' is derived from a battle in Spain in 1732, but the building is much earlier, 15th century in fact, and the exposed timbers and particularly the inglenook fireplace contribute their part to a warm and friendly air. A garden with barbecue should be established by the summer of '92, which is good news for those with children, for whom at present the pub, by its nature, is not really suitable. Featured in the CAMRA good beer guide.

THE WALNUT TREE

Yalding Hill, Yalding.   Tel. (0622) 814266

Location:	Village centre, on main road.
Credit Cards:	Access, Visa, Diners, Amex.
Accommodation:	2 doubles with tv, tea & coffee. From £26 per room.
Bitters:	Hook Norton, Fremlins.
Lagers:	Heineken, Stella Artois.

Examples of bar meals (lunch & evening, 7 days): *venison burgers, steak, curries, scampi, plaice, cod, vegetarian dish, salads, ploughman's, sandwiches, dish of the day.*
Examples of restaurant meals (as above): *sweet & sour trout, pork Walnut Tree, gingerstone swordfish, fillet steak, zrazie Nelson, roast duck jubilee, nutty courgettes with piquant sauce, veg roulade. Trad. Sun. roasts.*

There is actually a walnut tree in the garden, the fruits of which are used in the home cooking - a blend of the traditional and the exotic. An exceptionally good wine list includes a 1959 Chateau Latour (£200), though there are ofcourse many more modestly priced. Also exceptional is the live jazz laid on monthly; top nationally known musicians perform, and the landlord himself plays the bass. It is not known whether the resident ghost approves - a glass has been seen to fly, but he is apparently otherwise harmless. He (or she) could have lived here 500 years ago, when it was yeomen's cottages, and would still feel quite at home amongst the original timbers and large inglenook, lit in winter. The restaurant is particularly attractive. Children are permitted, and there's a large front patio. The pub stands on the Blossom Trail, and Leeds Castle is not far.

THE RINGLESTONE INN

Ringlestone, nr Harrietsham.   Tel. (0622) 859900

Location:	Junction 8 off M20, B2163 toward Sittingbourne, turn east at watertower north of Hollingbourne towards Doddington, straight ahead at next crossroads.
Credit cards:	Access, Visa, Diners, Amex.
Bitters:	Everchanging selection of eight.
Lagers:	Everchanging selection of six.

Examples from lunchtime buffet (7 days): *lamb & stilton pie, cod & prawn fish bake, spiced chicken casserole, lamb & coconut curry, salads. Brandy bread pudding, fruit crumble, treacle nut tart, homemade cheesecake.*

Examples from evening menu (7 days): *some dishes as above, rump steak in red wine sauce, grilled plaice topped with mango chutney & bananas, pork spare ribs in barbecue sauce, pizza pie, lasagne, chilli, jacket potatoes, ploughman's. Clotted cream ice creams.*

"A Ryghte Joyouse and welcome greetynge to ye all" says the inscription carved in 1632 on the oak sideboard. A previous notorious landlady took this to mean waving a shotgun at any stranger to whom she did not take a fancy, but fortunately the current landlord (for seven years) is rather friendlier. Otherwise much of the inn has changed little since it was built as a monks' hospice in 1533, and the massive dark timbers and well worn brick floors are clearly original. It is hard to credit that it stood on a busy thoroughfare, for it is now very much off the beaten track. One concession to the 20th century is the excellent lunchtime buffet, well suited to business people in a hurry. Supervised children welcome, and the lovely two acre garden has waterfalls and ample seating. Private parties arranged.

13

THE LEATHER BOTTLE

The Street, Cobham, nr Gravesend.   Tel. (0474) 814327

Location:	Village centre, on main road.
Credit cards:	Access, Visa, Diners, Amex.
Accommodation:	2 singles, 2 doubles, 1 twin, 2 4-posters. Some en suite, all with good facilities. From £37 single, £54 double. Special weekend breaks.
Bitters:	Ruddles County, Websters.
Lagers:	Carlsberg, Holsten Export, Kaliber.

Examples of bar meals (lunch & evening, 7 days): *beef & Guinness, roast topside, homemade shepherds pie, ham & mushroom pie, vegetable bake, salad bar.*
Examples of restaurant meals (as above): *steaks, chicken & stilton roulade, lemon sole with prawn sauce, medallions of pork finished in light cream & white wine sauce, rainbow trout in almonds. Trad. Sun. roasts.*

Dickens made mention of this lovely old inn in 'Pickwick Papers', and drank here himself - Dickens memorabilia is everywhere, generating the atmosphere of those times. It precedes him by several centuries (built 1629), and was a royalist meeting place during the Civil War. It acquired its name when a leather bottle containing gold sovereigns was found around 1720. Landlord Michael Eakins and staff welcome children, and in the large garden is 'Bumbles Teashop', open Sundays and Bank Hols. This is a marvellous spot for a stay, being quietly situated just minutes from the M2. Just opposite is Cobham Church, considered to be the best in the country for brass rubbings, and Cobham Hall is an easy walk.

THE WHITE LION

The Street, Selling, nr Faversham.   Tel. (0227) 752211

Location: Village centre.
Credit cards: Visa.
Bitters: Shepherd Neame Master Brew, Bishop's finger. Draught mild.
Lagers: Hurliman, Steinbeck, Steinbeck LA.

Examples of bar/restaurant meals (lunch & evening, 7 days): *homemade suet beef pudding, steak kidney & mushroom pie, steaks, scampi, plaice, chicken in rich peanut sauce, chicken & coconut curry, mushrooms in spicy provencal sauce with cheese topping, veg samosas with chilli sauce, ploughman's, sandwiches, daily specials. Homemade lemon meringue, fruit pies, sherry trifle, death by chocolate, treacle & nut tart. Trad. Sun. roasts.*

"Kent Village Pub of the Year" (Calor Gas) award winners, and featured on the front cover of the Boulogne guide to England - such approbation suggests this is no run-of-the-mill pub. Indeed, many customers travel miles for the delicious homecooked food, the beef or steak and kidney puddings being a particular favourite. Also popular are curry evenings on Mondays. Those booking in the restaurant for a special occasion are given a complimentary celebration fruit cake - typical of the warm welcome from Jackie and Tony Richards and staff. On Tuesdays the old ships' timbers of this 17th century coaching inn shake to the strains of live jazz, Tony himself playing the trumpet. A spit in one of the fireplaces is, unusually, operated by a water wheel, and also of interest is a collection of antique plates and teapots. Children welcome, pets corner in garden.

The Ship Inn and Smugglers Restaurant

THE SHIP INN & SMUGGLERS RESTAURANT

Conyer, Teynham, nr Sittingbourne.   Tel. (0795) 521404

Location:	Waterside, 2 miles from A2, signposted from Teynham.
Credit cards:	Access, Visa.
Bitters:	5 handpumps changed continually: Adnams, Batemans, Boddingtons, Brakspears, Camerons, Chas Wells, Courage Directors, Eldridge Pope, Everards, Fremlins, Flowers, Fullers, Gales, Goachers, Greene King, Harveys, King & Barnes, Marstons, Ruddles, Shepherd Neame, Theakstons, Wadworth, Whitbread, Youngers, Youngs.
Lagers:	9 taps rotating: Becks, Budweiser, Carlsberg, Grolsch, Heineken, Heineken Export, Holsten, Hurlimann, Kronenbourg, Lowenbrau, Moosehead, Stella Artois. Plus Biddenden cider.

Examples of bar meals (lunch & evening, 7 days): *local oysters, dressed crab, rainbow trout, homemade pies, curry, chilli, vegetarian dishes, wide range of ploughman's, toasted sandwiches, deep fried basket meals.*
Examples of restaurant meals (as above): *lobster thermidor, Dover sole, many steak dishes, wide range of seafood platters, moules mariniere, swordfish, game, daily specials.*

Built in the reign of Charles I, the inn was the centre of local smuggling activities over two centuries in this little backwater off the Swale, as in a hundred other quiet creeks along the Kent coast. The Smugglers Restaurant captures something of the spirit of those times, and 'The Dungeon' and 'Smugglers Store' dining areas are invested with a unique atmosphere. Of the extensive menu, it was the editor of 'Food & Drink' magazine who wrote, "In truth, I have had but a handful of memorable visits to table in 20 years of following the dubious profession of eating for a living. On the day of my visit to The Ship Inn & Smugglers Restaurant, I had one of the most memorable meals of my life."

The good food and wide range of dishes available both as bar snacks and in the restaurant is supported by a truly magnificent wine list, for which Alec and Lindsay Heard have received three major awards. The most recent of these was Les Routiers' 'Mercier Champagne Corps d'Elite 1991' award for outstanding wine list. Customers preferring beer as their beverage will have chosen well in seeking out this little creekside watering hole. Beside the range of draught beers and lagers there is a collection of more than 50 bottled beers from around the world to try. With 250 whiskies, 150 liqueurs, 50 brandies, 50 rums and a wide range of ports, for the connoisseur and novice alike, this is a most remarkable hostlery. In a word, it is unsurpassed for choice in the county.

THE QUEEN'S ARMS

Egerton Forstal, nr Ashford.   Tel. (0233) 76386

Location: Near Pluckley and Smarden.
Credit cards: Not accepted.
Bitters: Stonehenge, Adnams, Eagle (Bombardier in winter), Badger, Batemans Mild, guest.
Lagers: Red Stripe, Carlsberg.

Examples of bar meals (lunch & evening, 7 days): *homemade cottage pie, chicken ham & leek pie, fresh plaice, local sausages, prawn salad, homecooked ham, Welsh/buck rarebit, soft roes on toast, sandwiches. Evenings only: steaks, jugged hare, stuffed heart, gammon, homemade pies. Trad. Sun. lunches.*

The name of Bombardier Billy Wells will be familiar to connoisseurs of 'real' ales, who will be interested to know that landlady Valerie is his daughter. She and Tony have been pulling some very good pints here for about four years, and also enjoy a name for homecooked food. They run one of Kent's most agreeable country pubs, tucked away down leafy lanes in the heart of the rolling countryside, made famous by "Darling Buds of May". The tv series was filmed in these parts, and actors and other famous faces are not infrequently seen in the bars or dining room. There's always a friendly feel to the place, most especially at Sunday lunchtime, when there's live entertainmemnt. Children are welcome, and summer barbecues are held in the lovely garden. Pool table and darts.

THE RED LION

Hernhill, nr Faversham.   Tel. (0227) 751207

Location: On village green, not far off M2.
Credit cards: Access, Visa.
Bitters: Shepherd Neame Master Brew, Fullers London Pride, Marston's Pedigree.
Lagers: Hurlimanns, Heineken. Plus Theobalds cider.

Examples of bar meals (lunch & evening, 7 days): *curry, scampi, spaghetti bolognese, Yorkshire pudding with steak & kidney filling, lion burger, chilli, omelettes, salads, ploughman's, sandwiches, daily specials eg chicken in white wine sauce.*
Examples of restaurant meals (lunch & evening except Mons): *trout filled with prawns, butterfly chicken, pork chops in apple & calvados sauce, sirloin steak, Dover sole, vegetarian dish. Trad. Sun. roasts.*

It is always a pleasure to see an old building revitalised and given fresh purpose. Landlord Michael White has done just that with this 14th century Hall House, opening for trade only in December 1990. Holding up the entire edifice is a king post, quite rare, and visible in the upstairs restaurant - a splendid room, thickly carpeted, with vaulted ceiling and giant potted plants, suitable for a wedding reception etc. The bar has both woodblock and flagstoned floors, fine exposed brickwork and timbers, and log fires. 'Obadiah', a deceased ex-landlord is said to walk, but seems to trouble nobody. A pianist tickles the ivories on Fridays, and there's usually other entertainment on Tuesdays. The large garden has a play area (children also welcome inside) and bat-and-trap. Barbecues held Sundays and bank holidays.

THE GOLDEN LION

Mayton Lane, Broad Oak, nr Canterbury.   Tel. (0227) 710454

         Location: Village centre, 3 miles from Canterbury.
   Credit cards: Access, Visa, Diners, Amex.
         Bitters: Shepherd Neame Masterbrew, Spitfire, Abbey.
         Lagers: Hurlimann, Steinbock, Steinbock LA.

Examples of bar meals (lunch & evening, 7 days): *swordfish, 32oz rump steak, rack of ribs, chicken Hawaian, pork in red wine, leg of lamb, beef chop. Trad. Sun. roasts £3.95.* Restaurant planned for 1991 - bookings taken.

Renowned for good food and extensive, interesting menu, this former hunting lodge gets very busy, so it may be as well to arrive early to ensure a table. Despite the demand, prices remain very reasonable indeed - swordfish at £3.50, or chicken Hawaian at £2.50, for example. Neither are portions stinting - Trevor and Ann Jones have, in just a year or so, acquired an excellent reputation for quality and value. Hence in summer many large companies avail themselves of buffet lunches and hire the bat and trap pitches for in house competitions. Children will be amused by pets' corner, with rabbits, cockatiels, budgies guineae pigs etc., and the playground in the large garden. Barbecues are also held here, and there's seating for up to 100. Indoor entertainment includes darts, pool and shut-the-box. Ample parking.

THE RISING SUN

The Street, East Stourmouth, nr Wingham.   Tel. (0227) 722220

Location:	Village centre on B2046.
Credit cards:	Access, Visa, Mastercard.
Accommodation:	2 singles, 2 doubles, all with showers. Residents' lounge. Special winter breaks.
Bitters:	Four or five everchanging guests.
Lagers:	Four or five everchanging guests.

Examples of bar meals (lunch & evening, 7 days): *homemade steak & kidney pie, fish 'catch of the day', seafood fries, T-bone steak, daily specials.*
Examples of restaurant meals (as above): *steak and kidney pie, salmon steaks, steaks & grills, catch of the day, grilled rainbow trout, traditional Sunday lunch.*

During its 400 years or so, the inn has been a ferry house and a bakery to the old priory, but is now firmly established as a popular hostelry, noted for good food and for the local Theobald's cider. The ghostly figure of a man has reportedly been seen by both licensees and customers, but there is certainly no chill in the cosy 'olde worlde' bar and two dining rooms. Log fires cast a warm glow over the exposed brickwork and beams, and collections of plates, jugs and miniature bottles. Entertainment comes in the form of darts, pool or dominoes, and occasional special evenings. Children will enjoy the games room, and Bat and Trap is good fun in the garden. Dogs permitted by arrangement. Function room. Howlett Zoo, Blean Bird Park and ofcourse Canterbury are within easy reach.

THE SIX BELLS INN

Church Lane, Chislet, nr Canterbury.   Tel. (0227) 86373
- Location: 1 mile off A28.
- Credit cards: Not accepted.
- Bitters: Ruddles Best, Shepherd Neame Master Brew, Spitfire, Websters, guests.
- Lagers: Carlsberg, Fosters, Holsten Export, Hurlimanns, Kaliber.

Examples of bar meals (lunch & evening, except Sun evening): *fisherman's pie, seafood platter, steaks, chilli, omelettes, jacket potatoes, salads, ploughman's, sandwiches, daily specials.*

Examples of restaurant meals (evenings Tues - Sat): *grilled plaice with creamed prawn sauce, T-bone steak, poached salmon trout with mushroom filling, duck a l'orange, beef stroganoff, game casserole, venison in claret sauce. Trad. Sun. lunch £5.50 (children £3.50).*

There was a time when public houses were almost exclusively a male domain, and this holds true for some even today. But the family ownership of Jim, John and Sonja Hammond have engendered a family atmosphere over the past 18 months. Youngsters are always welcome, and the large garden has animals and duck pond. Karaoke and disco evenings are lively affairs (there's also live music Sunday and Friday evenings), barbecues are good fun, the outside bar and disco are for hire, there's a weekly meat raffle, bootfairs etc. The 50-seater cellar restaurant is available for functions. The more sedate and serious pleasures of good food and ale are not overlooked, as at least one national guide will testify. Incidentally, the pub is Georgian, and takes its name from the local church bells. Pool and darts. Parking for 30.

THE FORDWICH ARMS

King Street, Fordwich, nr Canterbury.   Tel. (0227) 710444

Location: ¼ mile off A28 at Sturry.
Credit cards: Not accepted.
Bitters: Whitbreads Best, Fremlins, Marston's Pedigree, Boddington's.
Lagers: Stella Artois, Heineken.

Examples of bar meals (lunch & evening, except Sundays): *homemade soups, moussaka, lasagne, Dorset onion & potato pie, Mr Nye's sausages in tomato sauce, beef curry, chicken in orange & walnut sauce, smoked haddock au gratin, giant New Zealand mussels in wine & garlic, ploughman's.*

You could be eating trout within 15 minutes of seeing it caught, for the river Stour flows past garden and patio. There can be few more agreeable spots to enjoy fresh food with a pint of Kent's finest, even if inclement weather drives you inside. Here you will find a jolly atmosphere, chatter undisturbed by mind-assaulting juke boxes etc, and a sturdy timbered Tudor style interior which surprisingly dates from 1930. Log fires warm both bar and dining room (available for functions), and there's a family room. Built over an old well into which criminals were once cast to die, it stands opposite the town hall, which was the courthouse. Nigel (ex navy chef) and Patsy (ex dancer) Thompson came here from The Anchor, Littlebourne, in March 1990, and are again establishing a reputation for one of the area's best eating houses. Bit tricky to find, but well worth the effort.

THE THREE TUNS INN

Staple, nr Canterbury.   Tel. (0304) 812317

Location:	Village centre.
Credit cards:	Access, Visa.
Accommodation:	3 doubles, 1 family, all en suite and recently refurbished. From £25 single, £40 double. Special terms for longer stays.
Bitters:	Fremlins, Whitbread, John Smith.
Lagers:	Heineken, Stella Artois, Fosters.

Examples of bar meals (lunch & evening, 7 days): *garlic prawns, rainbow trout with almonds, steak & kidney pie, chilli, steak, mixed grill, fresh cut gammon, cod, scampi, salads, ploughman's, sandwiches, daily specials.*

Examples of restaurant meals (every evening): *variety of steaks up to 32ozs, duck a l'orange, beef stroganoff, grilled plaice on the bone, roast chicken. Trad. Sun. roasts.*

Will you take up the 'house challenge'? - a 32ozs rump steak, unassisted. The mixed grill is also definitely not for the faint hearted. But the more health conscious appreciate the freshly pressed orange juice on the bar, especially in summer. With such thoughtful touches, Richard and Barbara Gunner, with son John and daughter Debbie, have built their success over 13 years. Beginning in 1712 as a farmhouse, the interesting history of The Three Tuns is well documented. It has undergone many changes, but without loss of charm, and indeed recent refurbishment of the low beamed bedrooms has made this a very pleasant place in which to stay. Children are welcome, and have swings and 2½ acres on which to romp. Staple vineyard, open to visitors, is nearby, and the wine may be purchased at the inn.

THE DOLLS HOUSE

Elham Valley Road, Barham, nr Canterbury.   Tel. (0227) 831241
- Location: On B2065, middle of Elham Valley.
- Credit cards: Access, Visa.
- Bitters: Shepherd Neame Master Brew, Wadworth 6X, John Smiths, guests.
- Lagers: Stella Artois, Carling, Fosters, Heineken, Heineken Export, Tennents LA.

photo courtesy Adscene Publishing Ltd.

Examples of bar/restaurant meals (11am - 11pm daily): *Greek cheeses (speciality), homemade soups & pates, homemade pies (eg rabbit & cider, chicken & oyster), gazpacho, breast of duck with marmalade sauce, sole poached in wine, steak chasseur, scallop croustade, mushroom & onion stroganoff, daily specials. Trad. Sun. roasts.*

It used to be near impossible to get a good meal in England outside of normal hours, but here is a prime example of how things have improved. New licensees Ernest and Lynne Tweedie change their wide and varied menus regularly, and food is served all day in friendly informality, and in spotlessly clean surrounds. The exposed beams and inglenooks in lounge bar and two cottagey dining rooms indicate 17th century origins, but the name derives from the many dolls made by the mother of a previous landlord. Unfortunately they were destroyed (only pictures remain), and there are stories of unexplained 'bangs' in the night and objects moved. Piped music yields to live jazz and blues on Wednesdays and Sundays. Children are welcome, and there's a large landscaped garden. Bar billiards. Small parties and meetings catered for. Vineyard adjoins pub.

THE ANCHOR INN

High Street, Wingham.   Tel. (0227) 720229

          Location: Village centre.
       Credit cards: Not accepted.
     Accommodation: 2 doubles (1 en suite), 2 twins (£30), 1 family (£35).
                     Single let £20.
            Bitters: Fremlins, Flowers, Whitbread Best.
             Lagers: Stella Artois, Heineken, Heineken Export.

Examples of bar meals (lunch & evening, 7 days): *homemade chicken Kiev, chicken cordon bleu, scampi, selection of steaks, spaghetti carbonara, lasagne, spaghetti bolognese, daily specials eg homemade steak pie, scampi & prawn thermidor. Trad. Sun. roasts.*

An outdoor swimming pool is a rare facility for a pub, and quite a boon in our recent hot summers. But this 16th century inn has much else to offer: hearty homecooked food and a good atmosphere, darts, pool and bar billiards, and very popular monthly live jazz evenings featuring top acts. Jerry and Sam and Donna and Paul (a chef for 20 years) are a family, and have been here for just a year or two. They look set for a long stay if previous landlords are any guide - there have been only 24 since records began in 1673. They supposedly have a phantom cavalier for company, who walks the hallway but not, apparently, the cosy timbered bars. Children are welcome, and the patio has a bat and trap area. Proximity to Canterbury with its glorious cathedral, as well as other picturesque villages, means an overnight stay could be in order.

THE BLAZING DONKEY

Hay Hill, Ham, nr Sandwich.   Tel. (0304) 617362

Location: Off A256 from Eastry.
Credit cards: Access, Visa, Diners.
Bitters: Tetleys, Burtons, Master Brew, John Bull, King & Barnes.
Lagers: Various, Kaliber LA. Plus Addlestones & Copperhead Ciders.

Examples of bar meals (lunch & evening, except Sun. evening): *chicken du chef, lasagne, roast, cottage pie, ploughman's, salads, omelettes, daily specials.*
Examples of restaurant meals (lunch & evening, trad. Sun. lunch): *steaks, medallions of beef in port wine sauce, rack of lamb with onion & garlic, breast of duck with champagne & cream sauce, poached trout, vegetarian dishes.*

Fresh produce for the kitchen is grown in the pub's own greenhouse, and the landscaped garden/patio is exceptionally large and well maintained. One side of the 300-year-old building is covered in a colourful mural, and extensions and modernisations have been tastefully executed. The single bar has been furnished in cottage style, and the 90 seater dining room can serve equally as a function room for weddings and private parties. Country and Western, folk and jazz are performed live on a regular basis. Barbecues are served Sunday lunchtimes and Saturday, weather permitting. The management welcomes children (and dogs) if well behaved, and the play area has swings, slide and bouncy castle.

27

THE TIGER INN

Stowting, nr Ashford.   Tel. (0303) 862130/862278

Location:	Off B2068 Hythe to Canterbury road.
Credit cards:	Access, Visa.
Bitters:	Everards Tiger, Greene King Abbot, Wadworth, Burtons, Tetley.
Lagers:	Lowenbrau, Stella Artois, Castlemaine.

Examples of bar meals (lunch & evening, 7 days): *homemade steak kidney & mushroom pie, cheesy smoked haddock & prawn pie (both noted), local trout, plaice, vegetarian choices, daily specials. Banana & Malibu nests, apple pie.*
Examples of restaurant meals (as above): *rack of lamb baked in breadcrumbs & herbs, poached wild salmon with dill & cream, mallard with bitter orange & brandy sauce, pheasant with green apples in cointreau & cream sauce. Brandy snaps with vanilla ice cream covered in brandy & ginger sauce. Trad. Sun. roasts in winter.*

At the foot of the North Downs, this homely 17th century inn is well placed for walkers and anyone who loves the lush, rolling countryside. In summer one can bask on the sunny terrace, in winter snuggle up to the fire, but do try the food - well above the norm, and a good range of beers, too. Menus are revised continually to reflect what is fresh and seasonal. The bar is redolent of a farmhouse kitchen, with posies of flowers, plates on the dresser and a scattering of cushions. The candlelit restaurant seats up to 30 and is bookable for private parties. Monday is jazz night, attended by other landlords on their night off, and red letter days like Halloween or New Year are marked by fancy dress do's. Alan and Linda Harris welcome well behaved children and organise weekend barbecues, weather permitting.

THE FLYING HORSE INN

Boughton Aluph, nr Ashford.   Tel. (0233) 620914

Location:	On village green.
Credit cards:	Access, Visa.
Accommodation:	3 doubles, 1 twin. TV's, central heating. From £30 b & b.
Bitters:	Courage Best & Directors, guest.
Lagers:	Fosters, Kronenbourg.

Examples of bar/restaurant meals (lunch & evening, 7 days): *homemade steak & kidney pie, Russian fish pie, fresh poached salmon in tarragon sauce, grilled whole local plaice, liver & bacon, lasagne. Banana & yoghurt cheesecake, death by chocolate, fruit crumble. Trad. Sun. roasts.*

The thwack of leather on willow is one of summer's most delightful sounds (except to the bowler, perhaps), and it has been heard here for over 250 years. Generations of cricketers have repaired to this much loved inn with heartening continuity. But since the 15th century pilgrims to Canterbury have sought refreshment, for it stands on the Pilgrims Way. Over the past three years Howard and Christine Smith have maintained this long record of hospitality, having 12 previous successful years of innkeeping. Food is better than ever, always fresh and homecooked, and the menu revised daily. Brasses catch the glow of open fires in winter, and fresh flowers grace the single, pleasant bar all year. Bat and Trap (a Kentish game) is played in the garden, as is jazz in kind weather - barbecues, too. Children permitted in certain areas. Booking advised for rooms. Dining room let for functions.

YE OLDE GATE INN

162 New Dover Road, Canterbury.   Tel. (0227) 452154

Location:	Off old A2 - main access road from Dover.
Credit cards:	Access, Visa.
Accommodation:	3 doubles, 1 family (en suite), from £40 per room.
Bitters:	Adnams, Shepherd Neame Master Brew, Whitbread Best.
Lagers:	Hurlimann, Tuborg Gold.

Examples of bar meals (lunch & evening, except Sun evening): *wide selection includes shepherds pie, steak & kidney pie, fresh fish.* Examples of restaurant meals: *carvery every day, with choice of roast joints, plus other dishes.*

This was the site of the original tollgate, straddling Watling Street, one of the great Roman roads in Britain. The inn itself is 'only' about 200 years old, and there are the customary tales of hauntings. Complete refurbishment has successfully recreated a Victorian 'country style' ambience, but with a distinctive cosmopolitan flavour, for Canterbury ofcourse attracts many foreign visitors. Chris and Sandy Gear are friendly hosts, who have established this as one of the city's better pubs in just two years or so. They welcome children if eating, and have a garden with summer barbecue. Parking for 60 is a major asset, and the county cricket ground is nearby. Many plans are afoot for new accommodation and other developments, so watch this space!

Leeds Castle, near Maidstone

31

THE CHESTFIELD BARN 14th CENTURY FREEHOUSE & RESTAURANT

Chestfield Road, Chestfield, nr Whitstable. Tel. (0227) 793086

Location: Village centre, approx. ½ mile off A299.
Credit cards: Access, Visa.
Bitters: Fremlins, Bass Masterbrew, Worthington, Whitbread.
Lagers: Stella Artois, Heineken, Carling Black Label, Tennents Extra, Tennents LA.

Examples of bar meals (lunch & evening, 7 days): *spit roast chicken, jacket potatoes, salads, sandwiches, farrier's lunch (pate), ploughman's lunch, platter of prawns, smoked mackerel, daily specials.*
Examples of restaurant meals (as above): *hot garlic mussels, seafood platter (speciality), lobster thermidor, crab, prawn medley, fish of the day, pork escalopes, chicken chasseur, salmon steak, grilled Dover sole, surf & turf, steaks, vegetarian dish, daily specials. Sweets of the day. Children's menu. Trad. Sun. lunch (12 - 3pm) £8.95 (3 courses). Businessman's lunch (Mon - Fri) £6.45 (2 courses).*
NB Bar open 11am - 11pm Mon - Sat, 12 - 3pm & 7 - 10:30pm Sun.

It makes a super front cover, and is a firmly established and popular part of the north Kent scene, yet it was only about three years ago that this eye-catching 14th century tithe barn was converted into a freehouse and restaurant. In fact, it opened on Halloween Night, which is still celebrated.
Beneath the magnificent thatched roof is a forest of venerable old timbers and beams, decorated by old farm implements, brassware and antiques. Two especially pleasing features are the minstrels gallery overlooking the main restaurant and bar, and a fine inglenook with open log fire in winter. Attractive as they are, these are not responsible for filling seats (even midweek it is usually busy) so much as the first rate food, particularly seafood, which is very much the house speciality. Owner John Kray sees to it personally that this is fresh and of high quality by buying from Billingsgate himself at 3am! He has 30 years experience of the trade, and sons Steve and John share his enthusiasm for the family business, the hallmarks of which are courteousness and attention to customer needs. Nothing is to much trouble for them or the friendly staff. Modern ideas blend with long established traditions; Wednesday night is cocktail night, for example (the cocktail list numbers some exotic creations), and business people can avail themselves of an astonishingly good value two course lunch, speedily served.
Special mention must be made of the truly lovely landscaped gardens. Pride of place goes to the waterfall and pond, full of carp, which will delight children (who are allowed inside if eating). Some of their elders may be drawn to the adjacent golf club. The seaside town of Whitstable is very near, and Canterbury just a short drive.

The Chestfield Barn.

The Pantiles, Tunbridge Wells

SUSSEX

Cliffs near Eastbourne.

THE TOP O' THE HILL AT RYE

Rye Hill, Rye.   Tel. (0797) 223284

Location:	½ mile from centre of Rye on A268.
Credit cards:	Access, Visa.
Accommodation:	1 single, 5 doubles, 3 twins, 1 family. Tv's, hairdryers, tea & coffee, central heating. 6 rooms en suite.
Bitters:	King & Barnes, Youngs.
Lagers:	Carlsberg, Fosters, Holsten.

Examples of bar/restaurant meals (lunch & evening, 7 days): *steak & kidney pie, pork & apple marsala, seafood lasagne, steaks, chicken breast stuffed with creamy leek & stilton sauce, Chineses duck, seafood au gratin, vegetable chilli, curry, dish of the day, kid's delight. Trad. Sun. roasts.*

Without doubt, Rye (one of the cinque ports) is amongst England's loveliest towns. Less than 10 minutes walk from its cobbled streets, standing (as the name suggests) on top of a hill, this country house style inn, pretty as a picture, blends the elegant and sophisticated with the homely and informal. The restaurant, recognised as one of the leading in the area, utilises the best local seasonal game, and seafood brought in daily by the trawlers. The well appointed bedrooms have been tastefully modernised, with a cottage style annex adding six en suite (one with facilities for the disabled), affording comfort rather superior to that endured by the 200 soldiers billeted here during the Napoleonic wars! Hazel and Peter Haydon are the proud owners, who welcome children and have a garden and car park. Well placed for superb beaches and countryside.

THE KING'S HEAD INN

Udimore, nr Rye.   Tel. (0424) 882349
      Location: On B2089 (Battle road), 3 miles from Rye.
  Credit cards: Not accepted.
        Bitters: Adnams, Harveys, Fremlins, guests.
        Lagers: Wide and ever-changing choice.
N.B. Quality accommodation can be arranged in the area.

Examples of bar meals (lunch & evening, 7 days): *paellas, fondues (both cooked to order), mixed grills, steaks, rack of lamb, fresh mussels (free on the bar in season), soused herrings (in season), salads, omelettes, vegetable curries/pies. Trad. Sunday roasts (booking advised).*

Farmers are not noted for the modesty of their appetites, neither do they take kindly to anything but the freshest of produce, so it is no small tribute when so many of them make this their 'local', though of course it is also well frequented by others. Fresh mussels on the bar is a nice touch, but as soon as the season is over they are replaced by garlic bread or roast potatoes – there is no dependence on the freezer, and the menus vary accordingly. A family-run pub (Trevor, Anita, Philip, Samantha and Lindsay), it evolved around 1600 from a 'Wayside Waste' – homes built by feudal landlords on waste ground for their workers – and remains genuinely unspoilt. Of special note is a real nine-pin skittle alley, the game from which ten-pin bowling originated. Children are welcome, and barbecues are held in the lovely garden in kind weather. Large car park.

THE STAR INN

Norman's Bay, Pevensey.   Tel. (0323) 762648

  Location: On the bay.
  Credit cards: Access, Visa.
  Bitters: Harveys, Chas Wells Bombadier, Bass, Worthington, Youngs, Old Roger, Gales HSB, Tanglefoot, guests.
  Lagers: Red Stripe, Hofmeister, Warsteiner, Carling, Tennents Extra, Carlsberg Export.

Examples of bar/restaurant meals (lunch & evening, 7 days): *roast pheasant, poached salmon, steak & kidney pie, lamb Shrewsbury, chicken & asparagus pie, sausages in Yorkshire pudding, steaks, selection of fresh local fish, 6 vegetarian dishes, salads, ploughman's, baguettes, daily specials. 20 homemade desserts.*

The bloodiest of all battles between smugglers and customs men took place here one dark night in 1828. Although the blockade was broken, many lay dead, and an era which had lasted over 200 years was effectively at an end. The inn was almost 500 years old even then, but though renowned for its matchless smuggling connections, is today one of the most successful in the county on the strength of good home-cooking and ales. The two bars and 90-seater restaurant are well used, and the venerable beams shake a little to the syncopated rythmns of live jazz every Tuesday and Sunday lunchtime, but without detriment to the unique and ancient character. Custodians of all this history for the last eight years have been Francis and Mary Maynard, who welcome children and have a garden with play area and barbecue.

THE GOLDEN GALLEON

Exceat Bridge, Seaford.   Tel. (0323) 892247

Location:	On A259 towards Eastbourne.
Credit cards:	Not accepted.
Bitters:	Courage Best & Directors, Yorkshire, guest.
Lagers:	Kronenbourg, Hofmeister, Fosters.

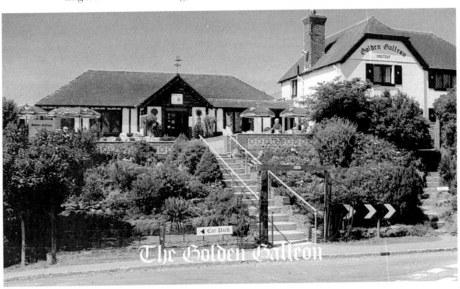

Examples of bar meals (lunch & evening, 7 days): *Italian seafood salad, bruschetta (garlic bread topped with plum tomatoes), chicken in tomato & fresh ginger sauce, fresh local fish, steaks, self-serve salad, ploughman's, daily specials eg pasta bake, lasagne, stilton & broccoli quiche.*

There's more than a touch of the Italian 'trattoria' here on this lovely stretch of coast, once earmarked as a likely invasion point from Europe. Proprietors Stefano and Lindsey Diella set out five years ago to blend the best of British with continental style, and would seem to have done so successfully, judging by their local popularity and the plaudits from national guides. Recently they were recipients of the 'Heartbeat' award for healthy eating and hygiene. Some Italian dishes, like lasagne, have been almost hijacked by the English, but Stefano says come and try the real thing! You will find yourself in an attractive bar cum dining room, half set aside for non-smokers, with high vaulted ceilings and timbers rescued from shipwrecks. On summer evenings you may prefer to take in the glorious views from the terrace, and perhaps develop an appetite with a leisurely stroll to the beach. Well behaved children welcome.

HANGLETON MANOR

Hangleton Valley Drive, Hove.   Tel. (0273) 413266

Location:	Outskirts of Hove, near golf course.
Credit cards:	Not accepted.
Accommodation:	B & B, en suite, from £45 per double room inclusive.
Bitters:	Hangleton Manor, Burton, Bass, Harveys, guests.
Lagers:	Lowenbrau, Carling, Castlemaine, Tennents, Tennents LA.

Examples of bar meals (lunchtimes Mon - Sat): *peppered smoked mackerel, quiche, jumbo sausages, chilli, lasagne, seafood pancake, ploughman's, sandwiches, daily specials.* NB There are plans to extend menu and serve evenings.

"Persevere ye perfect men, ever keep these precepts ten" - words carved here in oak with the ten commandments (the 17 letter "e's" were a sop to Elizabeth I). The distinguished history of the area's oldest house is described in a booklet, so suffice to say it is well documented in Domesday, and the 'modern' part dates from 1540. Both house and famous dovecote have been carefully restored to glory by Frank and Jennifer Saunders, lord and lady of Hangleton. The spirit of another lady, Jane, is said to walk, and that of a serving wench, seduced by the lord of the manor, who threw the resultant baby out of an attic window. But on Fridays the stately walls reverbrate to the sounds of disco, and there's regular folk and jazz, plus Morris dancing and medieval jousts. Family room and garden with play area. Great venue for weddings and other functions.

THE PELHAM ARMS

High Street, Lewes. Tel. (0273) 476149

Location:	Top of High Street.
Credit cards:	Access, Visa.
Bitters:	King & Barnes Sussex, Festive, Broadwood, Old Ale.
Lagers:	Castlemaine, Carling, Holsten Export.

Examples of bar meals (lunch & evening, Mon - Sat): *salads, ploughman's sandwiches, many homemade daily specials eg toad-in-the-hole, kedgeree, steak & kidney pie, ocean pie, chicken & mushroom pie, boiled beef & carrots, steak & walnut casserole. Homemade fruit pie, sherry trifle.*
Examples of restaurant meals (lunch & evening Tues - Sun lunch): *Sussex fish dish, Pelham pie, carbonnade of beef, fillet steak, escalope of veal in herbs & garlic, vegetarian & fish choices, daily specials. Pelham pot of chocolate, homemade meringue. Trad. Sun roasts & fish alternative.*

In the centre of this charming county town, The Pelham is well known throughout Sussex for the range of good local ales, outstanding home cooking and well above average wine list. Another important draw is the rather agreeable 'old world' atmosphere, established by the 17th century oak in the lounge and pine effect 'Sussex kitchen' in the restaurant area, warmed from a large open fireplace. It all once belonged to the Pelham family, and still has close associations with the horse racing fraternity, but Martin and Alison Shaw are pleased to welcome allcomers of all ages, from high chair to wheel chair. Sunday evening sees live entertainment, and barbecues are held in the car park in summer.

THE CROWN HOTEL

19 High Street, Hailsham. Tel. (0323) 843643

Location:	Town centre.
Credit cards:	Access, Visa, Diners.
Accommodation:	1 single, 1 double, 4 twins. Tv's, cntrl htng. £18.50 pp.
Bitters:	Theakstons XB, Courage Best & Directors, John Smiths.
Lagers:	Fosters, Kronenbourg.

Examples of bar meals (lunch & evening, 7 days): *homemade soup, roasts, breast of chicken (in onion, tarragon, wine & cream sauce), grilled trout.*

Examples from restaurant lunch menu (also available evenings in bar): *homemade steak & kidney pudding/pie, lasagne, farmhouse grill, garlic prawns, scampi, omelettes, jacket potatoes, ploughman's, weekly special.*

Examples from a la carte (lunch & evening, except Sun & Tues evenings): *scampi creole, steaks, rack of lamb, loin of pork Normandy, duck & orange sauce, Lantern veg pancakes. Trad. 4 course Sun lunch.*

When Barry and Carol Bridgen came here around four years ago they found a run down 17th century town centre pub. Calling on 20 years experience in the business (Barry was a catering lecturer), they have worked hard to build up a creditable concern. In particular, the Lantern Restaurant is a light, airy and pleasant room, with fresh flowers on each wooden table. The simple public bar has pool and darts, the informal lounge has bar billiards and open log fire. Anyone can join in Karaoke on alternate Saturday evenings, and a soloist/duo performs every Sunday lunchtime. To the rear is the Hall, once the Corn Exchange but now used for functions. Children welcome, but there's no garden. Car park.

THE NETHERFIELD ARMS

Netherfield, nr Battle.   Tel. (042 482) 282
       Location: Village centre.
    Credit cards: Visa, Access, Mastercard.
        Bitters: Courage Best & Directors, John Smiths.
        Lagers: Fosters, Hofmeister, Kronenbourg.

Examples of bar meals (lunch & evening, 7 days): *homemade soups, fried lemon sole, plaice, cod, salads, ploughman's, sandwiches, at least 8 daily specials, homemade steak & mushroom pie, fish pie, grilled gammon steak.*
Examples of restaurant meals (as above): *fresh salmon in asparagus sauce, steaks, escalope of veal in cream & herb sauce, duckling a l'orange, mixed grill, local venison, chicken Kiev, min. 8 vegetarian choices. Homemade chocolate & rum mousse, luxury fruit ice cream desserts. Trad. Sun. lunch (4 choices).*

"Pub of the Year", as nominated by a local newspaper in recognition of the first rate homecooked food, is a tribute to the 15 years in which Sandra and Richard Martin have established their pretty 16th century inn as one of the choicest in the area. Not far from the scene of the epic Battle of Hastings, it commands wonderful views clear to Beachy Head, almost 20 miles away. One can actually sit in the huge inglenooks, in which open fires crackle in winter, and there is a full quota of oak beams. Smokers and non-smokers are segregated in two separate restaurants, and vegetarians will find possibly one of the best selections in the region. Children are welcome, and barbecues are organised occasionally in the garden. Bodiam Castle, Battle Abbey and the lovely town of Rye are not far.

THE WAR-BILL-IN-TUN INN

Warbleton, nr Heathfield.   Tel. (0435) 830636

Location: Opposite church.
Credit cards: Access, Visa.
Bitters: Harveys Best, John Smiths, Old Ale in winter, guests.
Lagers: Holsten, Fosters, Stella Artois.

Examples of bar/restaurant meals (lunch & evening 7 days, but no bar food Sat evenings): *smoked oysters, salmon steak with seafood sauce, grilled trout with almond & wine sauce, steaks, Gressingham duck in orange sauce, veal escalope with mushroom & cream sauce, homemade steak & kidney pie, curry, scampi, salads, meat platters, blackboard specials. Apricot & brandy gateau, chocolate & rum gateau, banoffie pie. Trad. Sun. roasts.*

The odd name would seem to be a play on 'Warbleton' (said to be England's smallest village), but there is a story that it derives from civil war soldiers smashing open a barrel (or tun) with an axe. If that sounds unlikely there are many more tales about priest holes, sudden death and ghosts (a 17th century lady) which, sitting round the log fire in the depths of winter, do not seem too far fetched. Indeed, it would be unusual if an alehouse built in the late 13th century did not boast a few blood curdling stories, but none will detract from the enjoyment of the first rate cooking and convivial atmosphere which has won a place in local affections and national guides. Credit for this goes to Bryan and Valerie Whitton, who've served behind their serpent-shaped bar for over five years. Children welcome by arrangement, garden to front and rear.

THE SHEFFIELD COACH HOUSE

Sheffield Green, Danehill.　　　　　　　　　　Tel. (0825) 790245

Location:　On A275 from East Grinstead to Lewes.
Credit cards:　Access, Mastercard, Visa, Amex.
Bitters:　Ruddles Best, Courage Directors & Best, Websters.
Lagers:　Holsten, Fosters, Castlemaine, Budweiser.

Examples of bar meals (lunchtime, 7 days): *homemade soups, old fashioned steak & kidney pie, devilled kidneys, lasagne, scampi, seafood mornay, plaice, beef stroganoff, vegetarian dishes, daily specials, children's choice. Evenings: sandwiches, basket meals, jacket potatoes.*
Examples of restaurant meals (lunch & evening, 7 days): *asparagus pancakes, smoked salmon with prawn & tuna mousse; crispy layered mushrooms, seafood blanquette, fillet steak & scampi kebab, lamb Sheffield (on crouton with pate), duckling Coach House. Trad. Sun. roasts.*

Sheffield Park Gardens are especially lovely in autumn, and you will likely have seen them depicted in books and calendars. Part of the estate, the 18th century coaching inn stands less than one mile from them and the famous Bluebell steam railway. But this freehouse has attractions of its own: a skittle alley can take parties of 20-40 (basket meals included), and the restaurant is ideal for weddings and other functions. The three bars, timbered with open fires and brickwork, each have a theme: the Cricketers, the Dickens (with shove ha'penny etc) and the Stable (with satellite music tv, juke box, pool & darts). There's jazz club every Sunday evening, and regular dinner dances. Children are welcome, and have play equipment in the six acre garden, where barbecues are a regular summer event.

THE HALFWAY HOUSE

Rose Hill, Isfield, nr Uckfield.   Tel. (082 575) 382

Location:	On A26 between Uckfield and Lewes.
Credit cards:	Not accepted.
Bitters:	Harveys Best, IPA & Old.
Lagers:	Carling, Tuborg.

Examples of bar meals (lunch & evening, 7 days): *large variety of steaks with or without sauces, lobster, lemon sole, Dover sole, trout, fresh salmon in sauce, halibut, cod, scampi, seafood platter, mussels, langoustines, turkey & ham pie, steak & kidney pie, curry, lasagne, omelettes, vegetarian quiche, vegetable pie, salads, ploughman's.*

'Halfway' between Tunbridge Wells and Brighton, this 17th century coaching inn has long been a favourite stop for the weary traveller seeking rest and refreshment. In winter warm yourself by the real fires, as generations before have done, and absorb the cottagey atmosphere under the same sturdy timbers. Darts, pool, dominoes, and scrabble are amongst the diversions, or in summer you may see a classic car auction. The large, attractive garden has plenty of seating, and ball games may be played in an adjoining field. The range and quality of the food far surpasses that known to travellers past, seafood being a speciality, and the ale is rated by a national good beer guide. Although there is no formal restaurant, tables are laid up and may be reserved. Licensees of four years, Mike and Caroline Simpson, welcome children, and organise barbecues and other seasonal activities.

THE BRICKLAYER'S ARMS

Allington Road, Newick.   Tel. (082 572) 2976
     Location: 400 yds off A272 (turn right before Newick if approaching
               from Chailey).
Credit cards: Access, Visa, Mastercard.
     Bitters: Harveys Best, Ruddles County, Yorkshire.
     Lagers: Holsten, Carlsberg, Fosters.

Examples of bar/restaurant meals (11am to 10pm Mon - Sat., 12 to 3pm & 7 to 10:30pm Suns): *seafood pancake with cheesy topping, steaks, stuffed trout in wine sauce, fillet of plaice in shrimp sauce, homemade pies (eg steak kidney & ale, rabbit, chicken & broccoli), watercress & lamb bake, veal slices in herb sauce, pheasant in red wine with chestnuts, sweet & sour pork, spiced chicken in curry sauce, cheesy potato pie, veg lasagne, salads, jacket potatoes, sandwiches, ploughman's. Homemade desserts. Trad. Sun. roasts.*

The Professional Catering Guild numbers amongst its members Nigel and Sarah, licensees here since spring 1990. Their expertise is evident from a scan of the large and diverse menu, clearly well above normal pub fare. There is also the considerable blessing of extended hours in which to enjoy it. The six amiable cats who reside at this 19th century pub (who know when they're well off) are indifferent to the exposed timbers, original paintings, collection of cigarette cards and polished wood tables, but not to the log fire and thick carpets, no doubt. Other livestock consists of ducks on a pond and miniature goats in the garden - a delight to children, who are also permitted inside. Darts. Car park.

THE PLOUGH & HORSES

Walshes Road, Crowborough.   Tel. (0892) 652614

Location:	Between Crowborough and Jarvis Brook.
Credit cards:	Access, Visa.
Accommodation:	Bed & breakfast. All bedrooms with en suite facilities. (Feb 92)
Bitters:	Wadworth 6X, Youngs Special & IPA, Harveys, King & Barnes, Tetley.
Lagers:	Lowenbrau, Skol, Castlemaine, Tennents & Tennents Extra, Carling.

Examples of bar meals (lunch & evening, 7 days): *homemade soups, steak sandwich, omelettes, salads, ploughman's, daily specials.*

Examples of restaurant meals (as above): *steaks with various sauces, venison in rich red wine sauce, grilled halibut, Dover sole, Greenland wild salmon, trout meunière, roast poussin (in white wine, lemon & tarragon sauce), half roast duck in orange & morello cherry sauce, daily specials. Trad. Sun. roasts £8.95.*

This is Winnie the Pooh country, as immortalised by A.A. Milne, and the bridge over the little stream where he played 'Pooh sticks' is not far from here. It's a delightful corner of our countryside, on the edge of Ashdown Forest, and one of the highest points in Sussex. Tucked away down a country lane, yet only five minutes from Crowborough, this friendly old inn has been a labour of love for David and Brenda Newton, who have made it one of the most successful in the area, so that a further extension is now planned. Simple bar food is supplemented by a sizeable and diverse menu in the 48-seater restaurant, with a good, inexpensive wine list to match. Children have their own room, but in summer may prefer the garden with play area. Car parking.

THE DORSET ARMS

Withyham.   Tel. (0892) 770278

          Location: On B2110.
    Credit cards: Access, Visa.
         Bitters: Harveys Best, IPA.
          Lagers: Tuborg, Carling.

Examples of bar meals (French bread only Sun - Tues evenings): *lamb cutlets, chicken Kiev, scampi, plaice, jumbo sausages, veg lasagne, salads, ploughman's (noted), daily specials eg chicken in mustard sauce.*
Examples of restaurant meals (not Sun - Tues evenings): *deep fried brie with raspberry sauce, steaks, chicken stuffed with leek & stilton, grilled Dover sole, scampi provencale, trout. Homemade apple pie, crumbles. Trad. Sun. roasts.*

Lords and ladies rub shoulders with farm workers, and nobody puts on airs and graces at this unpretentious country pub. Built in 1556, it is named after the famous Sackville family, earls of Dorset, but there are more interesting tales to tell. Percy, a cavalier when he was alive, is said to generate his own 'ambience', and was even seen to stoke up the fire one night! An axe fell off the wall unaided recently, and on the day of the funeral of one of the regulars a robin flew in the bar and alighted on his chair, fulfilling an old superstition in these parts. If all this sounds a little spooky, it is in fact a notably relaxed place, with friendly bar staff and a chef who is prepared to be flexible to meet customer requirements. Children are welcome in the Delaware Restaurant (can be reserved for functions), where a now broken axe hangs over a fireplace unusual for having a window in it.

THE FOX & HOUNDS

Fox Hill, Haywards Heath.   Tel. (0444) 413342

Location:	On Ditchling road, approx 1 mile from town.
Credit cards:	Access, Visa, Diners, Amex.
Bitters:	Ruddles County & Best, Flowers Original, Websters Yorkshire.
Lagers:	Holsten, Carlsberg, Fosters.

Examples of bar/restaurant meals (lunch & evening, 7 days): *butterfly prawns, turkey ham & leek pie, steak & kidney pie, haddock & prawn smokies, curry, steaks, trout grilled with bacon, tomato & veg tagliatelle. Chocolate trufitos, charlotte russe, apple pie. Carvery Thurs - Sat evening & Sun lunch.*

Although not an unattractive building from the outside, the interior of this 16th century coaching inn is most agreeable. Its long, three-tiered lounge bar is overlooked by a gallery (with seating), and smartly polished wood is much in evidence. The arrangement of tables and chairs lends itself to conversation, but one section has bar billiards and there is also a children's room. The restaurant is a splendid room, with high vaulted ceiling and whirring fans, thickly carpeted floors and flowers on each table. A reputation for good food is well established, and the carvery is a popular feature. So, too, are barbecues, held in the pleasant, sheltered garden, which has a play area. Large car park. Not far from lovely Sheffield Park and Bluebell Railway.

THE THATCHED INN

Grand Avenue, Keymer, Hassocks.   Tel. (0273) 842946

Location: Edge of Keymer on Burgess Hill road.
Credit cards: Access, Visa.
Bitters: Harveys Sussex, Bass, IPA.
Lagers: Carling, Tennents.

Examples of bar meals (lunchtime 7 days, evenings Wed - Sat): *potato skins & chilli dip, garlic mushrooms, chicken satay & peanut sauce, homemade steak & kidney pie, steak in port & mushroom sauce (evenings only), fresh fish when available, vegetarian dishes. Selection of sweets. Trad. Sun. roasts.*

At the foot of the south downs, this picturesque thatched inn commands lovely views from its panoramic windows over rolling fields to the Ditchling Beacon. Built in 1952, it is one of the region's more recent pubs, and one of the more unusual - a fine example of what can be achieved with a little imagination. The thatch is of best Norfolk reeds, and perhaps most eyecatching inside is the huge 'herringbone' brick fireplace. The two bars together form a 'horseshoe', with the central area virtually a dining room and no-smoking area. Pool and darts are played in the public bar, and the third Tuesday of every month is folk music night. Ishbel and Edward Daniel have 20 years experience in the trade, the last 18 months attracting local support and passers by. They welcome children and have a good size garden with play area and barbecue. Sunday lunch especially popular.

THE CROWN

The Green, Horsted Keynes, nr Haywards Heath.   Tel. (0825) 790449

Location:	Village centre, five miles north of Haywards Heath.
Credit cards:	Visa, Mastercard.
Bitters:	Websters Yorkshire, Ruddles Best & County.
Lagers:	Holsten, Carlsberg, Fosters.

Examples of bar meals (lunch & evening, 7 days): *homemade steak & kidney pie, Chinese stir-fried prawns, homecooked ham & egg, French style mushroom crepes, mushroom & nut fetuccini, daily specials.*

Examples of restaurant meals (Fri & Sat evenings, Sun lunch): *mushroom provencale, whitebait with yoghurt & watercress dip, tiger prawns served with rice & stir-fry vegetables, sirloin steak with garlic prawns, breast of chicken in port wine & mushroom sauce, Crown grill. Trad Sun. roasts.*

There are some little-heard-of activities here for those who like a spot of recreation with their refreshments: a stoolball pitch, for example, along with cricket, and inside is a karaoke machine, plus pool and darts. Wednesday is the time to test the grey matter, when it's quiz night. The games are in the public bar, but the lounge bar is more conversational, with exposed timbers, inglenook fireplace and horsebrasses. Overlooking the cricket pitch is the restaurant, which is also decorated by brasses and horse saddles. Trevor, Karen, Jerry and Jackie arrived here in only summer 1990, but have 25 years experience in catering. They permit children and dogs, and have a garden and playground. Large car park. Bluebell Steam Railway and beautiful Sheffield Park nearby.

ANSTY CROSS

Cuckfield Road, Ansty, nr Haywards Heath.   Tel. (0444) 413038

          Location: Village centre, jncn of A272 with B2036.
   Credit cards: Access, Visa.
          Bitters: Ruddles County & Best, Websters.
          Lagers: Fosters, Carlsberg, Holsten Export.

Examples of bar meals (lunch & evening, 7 days): *chilli, pizza, steaks, mixed grill, chicken Kiev, Scottish salmon, lasagne, macaroni cheese with various toppings, sweet & sour pork, steak & kidney pie, self-serve salads, ploughman's, many daily specials eg tandoori chicken, tuna & cheese pie, homemade quiche. Banoffi pie, hot chocolate fudge cake, apple pie. Children's menu. Trad. Sun. roasts September to May.*

There has certainly been an inn at this busy crossroads since time immemorial, and this one was built around the turn of the century on the site of the 'Green Cross Inn' (the pub sign depicts a scene from the Bayeux tapestry showing the Conqueror with a papal banner bearing a green cross. The emblem was adopted by a local nobleman named Hussey). Its light, uncluttered interior, nicely furnished in pine, consists of a comfortable lounge bar, games room and pleasant 35-seater dining room (children welcome). The pub is run by Steve and Wendy Tickner, who since taking over in 1990 have concentrated on providing high quality meals in an informal, relaxed atmosphere. Much emphasis is placed on home-cooked dishes, whenever possible. Colourful, safe garden has play area. Car park.

THE FOUNTAIN INN

Ashurst, Steyning.   Tel. (0403) 710219
        Location: Village centre, on B2135.
    Credit cards: Not accepted.
         Bitters: Fremlins, Strong Country, Marston's Pedigree,
                     Flowers Original, 2 guests.
          Lagers: Stella Artois, Heineken.

Examples from lunch-
time menu (7 days):
*homemade steak &
kidney pie, cottage pie,
lasagne verdi, moussaka,
quiche, flans, sausages,
ploughman's, daily
specials.*
Examples from 'candlelit
supper' menu (not Wed
or Sun): *steaks, chicken
Kiev, turkey cordon bleu,
curry, scampi, cod.*

Voted 'Best Country Pub
in West Sussex' (1990)
in a competition org-
anised by The Brewers
Society and Brighton
Evening Argus; voted
no. 2 CAMRA pub in
the south of England
(1990); a regular in
good beer and pub

guides; used by Paul McCartney as a film location and by Laurence Olivier as his
'local'; clearly, here is no run-of-the-mill freehouse. For 13 years Maurice and Jean
Caine, both from an aviation background, have run this unspoilt 16th century inn,
full of character and atmosphere. Even the ghost is friendly, and has reportedly been
seen in daylight more than once. Low beams, flagstone floors and inglenooks are
unmistakably authentic. A jukebox would be sacrilege, but there are quieter pursuits
like shove ha'penny and crib. Children are allowed in the lounge if eating, and
there is a large garden with duck pond and play equipment. Plans are afoot for a
new restaurant.

THE BLUE SHIP

The Haven, Billingshurst.   Tel. (0403) 822709

            Location: Off road between Five Oaks (A29) and Bucks Green (A281).
        Credit cards: Not accepted.
             Bitters: King & Barnes Sussex, K & B Broadwood.
              Lagers: Carling, Holsten Export. Plus Stowford Press cider.

Examples of bar meals (lunch & evening, except Sun & Mon evenings): *homemade soups, cheesey cottage pie, ratatouille au gratin, lasagne, cod, plaice, scampi, steak & kidney pie, chilli, ploughman's, sandwiches. Fruit crumble, Granny's wedding cake, treacle tart, chocolate fudge cake.*

Others lay claim to being 'real country pubs', but here is the genuine article, built around 1500. Enter by a low door and a cheerful face will greet you at the servery hatch opposite. Beer is served direct from the casks, not pumped. At times the bar is full of working dogs and their owners, the once white ceilings are now yellow, and all is much as you might have found it around 1900. The solid old beams are bedecked with foreign banknotes, the floors are polished brick, and furniture is scrubbed wood. A games room has bar billiards and darts, and a small dining room is decorated with pictures of large dogs - landlady Jenny Davie has six Newfoundlands, and is a judge. She has also supervised the cooking since arriving three years ago with husband John. They welcome children and have a garden with play equipment. Featured in national good pub guide.

Sheffield Park Gardens

THE GEORGE & DRAGON

Burpham, nr Arundel.   Tel. (0903) 883131

Location:	At end of village (no through road).
Credit cards:	Access, Visa.
Bitters:	Harveys, Courage Directors, Ruddles County, 2 guests.
Lagers:	Fosters, Kronenebourg, Carlsberg.

Examples of bar meals (lunch & evening, except Sun evening): *fresh fish, shepherds pie, steak & kidney pie, bangers & mash, Swiss rosti, many daily specials eg beef rollantine & noodles, fresh skate, lamb curry. Spotted dick.*

Examples of restaurant meals (evenings except Sun): *exotic seafood salad, game roulade wrapped around avocado; escalopes of veal filled with apricots & served with marsala sauce, breast of magret duckling (with orange, brandy & kumquat sauce), Scotch fillet (on bed of leeks & onions in filo pastry topped with mozarella), scallops with pernod & cream sauce. Trad. Sun lunch.*

One of the most enjoyable drives to any pub is rewarded by lovely views over Arundel Castle to the sea beyond, but many arrive at this exquisite little village by foot, for here is some of the best walking country in the region. The road leads nowhere else, but walkers and motorists alike are drawn by this likeable 18th century pub, noted for first class cooking and choice ales. The bar menu is chalked up daily on a board, and other framed reading matter desribes the history of the place. The single bar has an antique grandfather clock, coal fire and a little gallery area. The bright, bay windowed restaurant has flowers on each table, crisp white linen and large inglenook - and look for the old twister (not the landlord, but a gaming device on the ceiling). Amiable proprietors George and Marianne Walker allow well behaved children. Recommended by most main guides.

THE FOX INN

Bucks Green, Rudgwick.　　　　　　　　　　　　　　Tel. (0403) 822386

       Location: On A281 Horsham to Guildford road.
    Credit cards: Not accepted.
       Bitters: King & Barnes Best, Sussex, Broadwood, Festive, Old Ale.
       Lagers: Carling, Holsten Export. Plus Stowford Press cider.

Examples of bar meals (lunch & evening, except Sun evening): *homemade soups, beef teryaki (noted), grilled trout stuffed with prawns, homemade chicken Kiev, steaks, pizzas, burgers, lasagne, scampi, plaice, leeks in mustard sauce, vegetable pie, jacket potatoes, salads, ploughman's, sandwiches. Banana split, death by chocolate, sorbets. Children's menu. Trad. Sun. roasts in winter.*

Once a year a pony is led through the inn, to acknowledge a bridleway between front and back doors. Other time-honoured traditions are also well observed at this friendly village local, formerly 16th century cottages. Pauline (ex air-hostess) and Charlie (ex restaurateur) serve a wide range of fresh, homecooked food, English and international, plus excellent beers. In 1930 the son of the then landlord died, and is said to return every Boxing Day. He will find it warm and comfortable, the saloon bar dominated by a large inglenook, and the main bar with its collections of books, bottles and pictures. A small games room has pool, darts and skittles, quiz nights are held on the first Sunday of the month, and local groups perform on Wednesday evenings. Children are welcome in the large garden which has climbing frame and swings, and barbecues Sunday lunchtimes in summer.

THE FOX GOES FREE

Charlton, nr Chichester.   Tel. (0243 63) 461
          Location: Village centre, 1 mile east of A286, near Goodwood.
      Credit cards: Access, Visa, Amex.
   Accommodation: 2 twins en suite. £22.50 single, £34.50 double incl.
                     Special 'Glorious Goodwood' breaks £50 per room.
           Bitters: Ringwood Old Thumper, Abotts Ale, Ballards Best & Wassail,
                     Flowers, Marston's Pedigree, Batemans.
           Lagers: Stella Artois, Heineken. Plus Scrumpy Jack cider.

Examples of bar meals (lunch & evening, 7 days): *homemade steak & mushroom pie, curry, lasagne, quiche, jacket potatoes, ploughman's, sandwiches, daily specials eg game, crab, lobster in season. Children's menu.*
Examples of restaurant meals (as above): *shark steak (with shallot, mushroom & white wine sauce), wood pigeon with blackcurrant sauce, chicken breast stuffed with crab in seafood sauce, sirloin steak, savoury cashew nut balls. Trad. Sun. roasts.*

It sounds like good news for the quarry, but the name derives from when 'The Fox' became a free house in 1985. In the 16th century it was called 'The Pig & Whistle', renamed when the Duke of Richmond made hunting popular in these parts. Perhaps its main claim to fame is that the initiation and first meeting of the Womens Institute in England was held in what is now the Hat Rack bar, back in 1915. But it is not for history that the inn is so well liked, and featured in major good pub guides, rather for imaginative homecooked food, select ales and a pleasant atmosphere. Children are welcome, and the enormous garden (with barbecue) has sand pit, swing, and magnificent views over the south downs. Dining room available for functions. Bar skittles.

THE ROYAL OAK

Hooksway, Chilgrove.   Tel. (0243 59) 257

Location:	1½ miles north of Chilgrove, off B2414.
Credit cards:	Access, Visa, Diners, Amex.
Accommodation:	1 double, 4 twins, all en suite. £16 pp incl.
Bitters:	Ruddles County & Best, Gibbs Mews Bishop's Tipple, King & Barnes Festive, Websters Yorkshire, guests.
Lagers:	Holsten, Carlsberg. Plus Scrumpy Jack cider.

Examples of bar meals (lunch & evening, 7 days): *venison pie, steak & kidney pie, gammon, pizza, vegetable lasagne, baked potatoes, ploughman's, daily specials.*
Examples from Hideaway Restaurant menu (as above): *terrine of wood pigeon, ratatouille omelette with gruyere cheese, monkfish & vegetable parcels, steaks, roast guinea fowl, rack of lamb, roast saddle of rabbit on bed of spinach with port & mushroom sauce, medallions of venison served on crouton (topped with pate & coated with red wine sauce).*

You probably won't find Hooksway on your road map; at the foot of a narrow lane, surrounded by woods, it comprises just the 15th century pub, a house with accommodation, and the restaurant. But it is has been host to three monarchs, no less, together on the same shooting party, and to many thousands of humbler folk who come for the wonderful tranquility, good food and ales. Game naturally features prominently on the menu. The lower bar (or tap room) seats 20, has polished brick floor and is ideal for walkers. The main bar, beamed and with open fire, leads on to the new games room, with pool and darts. Live jazz is played on the last Friday of each month. Children are welcome, and the large garden has play equipment and barbecue.

THE RICHMOND ARMS

Mill Lane, West Ashling, nr Chichester.   Tel. (0243) 575730

Location: In village.
Credit cards: Not accepted.
Bitters: Everchanging guests; Marston's Pedigree, Timothy Taylor Landlord, Harveys Sussex Mild, Boddingtons, Brakspears, King & Barnes Festive, Thwaites Traditional.
Lagers: Edehall Export, Stella Artois, Heineken, Heineken Export.

Examples of bar meals (lunch & evening, 7 days): *chicken tikka, fish pie, local trout, mixed grill, steaks, stuffed plaice with prawns, chicken Kiev, Richmond burger, veg lasagne, vegetable pie, moussaka, rack of lamb, jacket potatoes, salads, ploughman's, sandwiches. Treacle pudding, hot chocolate fudge cake, fruit salad. Children's menu.*

An amazing 127 different real ales have passed through the pumps here in under one year since Bob and Chris took over, and 545 in the eight years before that. So it's a Mecca for beer drinkers, but there's much else besides. Built around 1850, this is not the most eyecatching of pubs, but nonetheless does not lack character, and is much in favour with actors from the Chichester theatre. Ducks form the main theme of decor, and the collection of decoys in the bar is used for an annual charity race down a local stream. Food is traditional and wholesome, with an already large menu about to be augmented with a vegetarian selecion. Theme nights like St Patrick's or Burns' add further novelty. Children are welcome, and by the car park is a patio with pergola. Praised by national good pub guide.

THE BLACK HORSE

Birdham Road, Apuldram, nr Chichester.   Tel. (0243) 784068

Location:	On A286.
Credit cards:	Access, Visa.
Bitters:	King & Barnes, Burtons, John Bull.
Lagers:	Lowenbrau, Castlemaine, Skol.

Examples of bar meals (lunch & evening, 7 days): *deep fried calamari, king prawns, baked camembert, deep fried seafood, lasagne, roasts, steaks & grills, jacket potatoes, salads, ploughman's, sandwiches, daily specials. Trad. Sun. roasts.*

"Always a warm welcome, and a great meal at a price that's right" - the declared aim of the management. The cheerful young staff do generate a friendly atmosphere, and the very sizeable menu is moderately priced. Although drawing trade on the way to the beaches of Wittering, it is also well frequented by locals. Built as cottages around 1775, it became a pub circa 1890, but its origins are clearly evident from the old beams, inglenooks and brickwork, decorated with agricultural implements. A separate dining area seats about 25, and the large garden with patio has benches and tables. Families are most welcome, and there's parking for about 60 cars. Chichester and its harbour are only about three miles away. Rated by CAMRA guide.

THE LAMB INN

West Wittering, nr Chichester.   Tel. (0243) 511105

Location: On B2179 beyond Birdham.
Credit cards: Not accepted.
Bitters: Ballards, Ringwood, Bunces, guests.
Lagers: Warsteiner, standard brands.

Examples from lunchtime menu (every day, snacks only on Sunday): *homemade steak & mushroom pie, smoked fish flan, lasagne, curry, fried fillet of plaice, chicken cordon bleu, vegetarian dish, ploughman's, toasted sandwiches, salad bar in season.*
Examples from evening menu (not Suns): *some dishes as above, sirloin steak, grilled fresh halibut/lemon sole/plaice/brill, salmon steak, gammon, vegetarian dish. Homemade apricot & almond tart, chocolate glu glu sponge, treacle tart.*

The dovecote in the rear garden actually appears to house pigeons, but otherwise it is hard to find fault with this 18th century inn, well run by Nigel and Jo Carter. Originally a cottage and forge, it became a pub in 1835. A favourite amongst sailors from Chichester harbour, holidaymakers from the sandy beaches and walkers from nearby East Head, the Lamb is also well regarded by locals and by national good pub guides. Home cooking and fine real ales have much to do with this, coupled with a warm atmosphere - especially when the log and coal fires are lit. The traditional style of the bar and dining rooms is complemented by attractive local photographs. The garden room offers a summer salad bar. Well behaved (!) children are welcome in the dining areas when eating a meal in adult company. Gardens. Car park.

Royal Pavilion, Brighton.

HMS Victory, Portsmouth.

THE WINE VAULTS

43-47 Albert Road, Southsea.   Tel. (0705) 864712

Location: Opposite King Theatre.
Credit cards: Access, Visa.
Bitters: Adnams, Bass, Boddingtons, Wadworth, plus up to 12 guests.
Lagers: None on draught.

Examples of bar meals (12-2pm weekdays, 2:30pm weekends, 5:30-7:30pm Mon-Sat): *'double breasted' jacket potatoes, salad bowls, large wholemeal rolls or French sticks, ploughman's, daily specials. Trad. Sun. roasts.*
Examples of restaurant meals (6-11pm Mon-Sat. Functions only at lunchtime): *ham cornets filled with Russian salad, ossiete de saumon fume, filets de sole au porto, cote de porc Normande, menthe claciale.*

The name is perhaps a little misleading, for it is the astonishing selection of 16 everchanging real ales, the largest in the area, for which the Wine Vaults is famed. To date, over 300 brands have been stocked, and it will come as no surprise that regular plaudits from CAMRA have been forthcoming. Connoisseurs should not miss the biannual beer festivals, and note that prices are reduced Monday evenings. But even those with no taste for beer will appreciate the good, fresh food (French chef) and bustling atmosphere. The interior is panelled throughout, has wooden floors, old fireplaces and seating on church pews. The upstairs restaurant (children welcome evenings) doubles as a function room, and the quieter of the two bars (children welcome lunchtimes) can also be reserved. Easy parking in street.

UNCLE TOM'S CABIN

48 Havant Road, Cosham.   Tel. (0705) 210145

Location: Near town centre.
Credit cards: Access, Visa, Amex.
Bitters: Gales HSB, Busters, BBB, South Down.
Lagers: Stella Artois, Fosters, Heineken.

Examples of bar meals (lunch & evening, 7 days): *steaks & grills, vegetarian lasagne, roast of the day, scampi, burgers, jacket potatoes, salads, ploughman's, sandwiches, daily specials eg steak & kidney pudding, chicken a la creme, pasta bake, plaice. Chocolate mountain cake, lemon tart.*

"We never forget you have a choice" - so proclaims the management on the extensive menu. It's a philosophy that has made this a lively and popular town centre pub, where families are especially welcome. Well placed for travellers on the way to Portsmouth, it is also enjoys a buoyant local trade, always the true test of a good pub. Built in the 50's to replace one of the same name, its one long bar seats 20, with plenty of room for standing, and a raised dining area seats 68, separated from the bar by decorative wrought iron railings. Carpeted throughout, its padded chairs, polished wood tables and numerous old prints lend the air of a 1930's town pub. Local groups perform sometimes, and quiz nights are well attended. A small front garden has seating for 24.

THE BAT & BALL

Broadhalfpenny Down, Hambledon.   Tel. (0705) 632692

       Location: At crossroads between Hambledon and Clanfield.
  Credit cards: Access, Visa, Diners, Amex.
         Bitters: Friary Meux, Burtons, John Bull. Ind Coope dark mild.
         Lagers: Castlemaine, Lowenbrau, Skol, Swan Light.

Examples of bar meals (lunch & evening, 7 days): *homemade steak & kidney pie/pudding, cottage pie, chicken & ham pie, lasagne, steaks, curries, roast chicken, plaice, scampi, cheese & onion pie, peanut bake, salads, ploughman's, sandwiches, daily specials.*
Examples of restaurant meals (as above): *steaks, venison in red wine, chicken Maryland, pheasant braised in red wine sauce, beef Wellington, chef's mixed grill, poached salmon with asparagus, lemon sole bonne femme, salads, vegetarian dishes. Trad. Sun. roasts - book two weeks ahead.*

The Bat and Ball occupies a hallowed place in the annals of cricket. From 1770 during the 'Hambledon Era' the club was chief authority in the game, its laws adopted nationally. Many big matches were played on the famous down against All England, and a replica scorecard of an especially heroic victory is one of many memorabilia on display. Having been the pavilion and clubhouse, the pub is a mecca to devotees of our cherished national sport. But most people who come do so for the high standards of food, service and relaxation - the advice to book at least two weeks ahead for Sunday lunch speaks volumes. Guardians of the 'shrine' are Bill and Jean Galbraith - Bill was Ind Coope Cellarman of 1989 and finalist in 1990. They accept children as 'seen but not heard'. Daytime functions in dining room.

YE OLDE GEORGE INN

Church Street, East Meon.   Tel. (0730) 87481
              Location: Village centre.
          Credit cards: Visa, Amex, Diners.
       Accommodation: 2 singles, 1 double, 1 twin, all en suite with TV's, tea & coffee.
              Bitters: Flowers Original, Strong Country, Boddingtons, Pompey Royal.
              Lagers: Stella Artois, Heineken.

Examples of bar/restaurant meals (lunch & evening, except Thurs evening): *homemade soups, steak kidney & mushroom pie, chicken & mushroom pie, Lancashire pastie, chilli, lasagne, chicken Kiev, macaroni cheese, curry, quiche, lemon sole, scampi, haddock, salads, ploughman's, jacket potatoes, daily specials. Children's menu. Trad. Sun. roasts.*

The unusual circular bar is surrounded by massive wooden farm furniture, and working harnesses on the walls - appropriately enough, for the Domesday Book lists a farm on this site, which brewed its own ale. The eponymous George is the patron saint of England (the sign shows him with dragon) - a fitting name for a fine example of an English country pub. Food is mostly homemade and fresh, and accompanied by an exceptional range of uncommon beers. Frederick and Dorothy Milnes have provided the hospitality at this 17th century inn since February 1990. One unofficial member of staff is allegedly the spectre of an old lady who likes to tidy up, but she hasn't been seen lately. Morris dancers perform here in season (ask for dates), and the Watercress Steam Railway is nearby. Children are welcome in the dining room, and the garden has an aviary.

THE TOLLHOUSE INN

Southampton Road, Buckland, nr Lymington.　　　　　Tel. (0590) 672142

Location:	On main road.
Credit cards:	Access, Visa, Eorocard, Mastercard.
Bitters:	Wadworth 6X, Whitbread, guest.
Lagers:	Stella Artois, Heineken, Heineken Export.

Examples of bar/restaurant meals (lunch & evening, 7 days): *beef & ale pie, Buckland bangers, roast, devilled kidneys, curry, butterflied chicken breast, honey roast lamb, pork in cider sauce, scampi, pancake specials, haddock & pasta bake, lasagne, prawn-filled trout, steaks, garlic melts on French bread, jacket potatoes, Danish open sandwiches, ploughman's, daily specials. Bananana pancake, profiteroles, blackberry & apple pie. Trad. Sun. roasts.*

Everything is cooked to order by landlady Deana Stevens, so there may be a little wait, but patience has its rewards. The comprehensive menu makes mouthwatering reading, whether one is seeking a simple snack or full meal, and may be enjoyed in bar or dining room. The latter is in the style of a medieval hall and, like the lounge, is timbered and panelled, with open log fire and carpets lending extra warmth. Look for the Tudor coat of arms of the Button family outside. The old tollhouse is in the grounds, but the pub itself dates from 1671 and was known as 'The Monkey House'. There's live entertainment some Sunday evenings, and occasional barbecues at weekends. Deana and husband Mike have a children's room and garden with patio. Isle of Wight ferry and Beaulieu House nearby.

THE FLEUR DE LYS

Pilley, Lymington.   Tel. (0590) 672158

Location:	Village centre.
Credit cards:	Access, Visa.
Bitters:	Boddingtons, Flowers Original, Wadworth 6X.
Lagers:	Heineken, Stella Artois.

Examples of bar meals (lunch & evening, 7 days): *salmon cucumber soup, Caribbean pork, chicken in redcurrant & pear, king prawns in apricot & brandy, perch in prawn sauce, duck in green peppercorn sauce, steak Diane, pasta bolgnese. 'Rigor Mortis', profiteroles, toasted lemon brulee.*

The examples given above are just a selection from a large and exciting menu, far superior to typical pub fare. Many of the dishes are to be found also at the New Forest Inn at Emery Down and the Trusty Servant at Minstead, all owned by Nick and Sue Emberley - a trio of super pubs in the depths of the New Forest. Ofcourse one can equally enjoy a simple snack, or just a good pint of ale in a friendly atmosphere. The two bars are intriguingly named 'Beverley of Arnwood' and 'Jacob of Armitage', both carpeted and comfortable, and the latter has a huge inglenook fireplace, as does the small, light dining room. The entrance passage is worth a special mention; original beams are set in an old tree root, and there is list of previous landlords - only 41 since 1498. Children are welcome, and the large mature garden has swings. Live piano is planned in near future.

THE RED LION

Boldre, Lymington.   Tel. (0590) 673177

Location: Village centre, ¼ mile off A335.
Credit cards: Access, Visa.
Bitters: Eldridge Pope Dorchester & Royal Oak.
Lagers: Faust, Kronenbourg.

Examples of bar meals (lunch & evening, 7 days): *homecooked gammon with poached eggs, half duckling with wine soaked orange slices, scampi, lamb cutlets with rosemary, vegetable casserole topped with cheese, salads, ploughman's, sandwiches. Homemade apple pie, sherry trifle, profiteroles, knickerbocker glory.*

"One cannot judge a book by its cover" - a wise epithet, but in this case what awaits inside lives up to the promise of the pretty exterior. The original cottage is recorded in Domesday as brewing and selling ale, but the inn dates from 1680, and stands on a river crossing by the village green on the edge of the New Forest. Mr and Mrs Bicknell have invested 16 years in making their business successful, the friendly atmosphere, good food and wine having earned a star rating in a major national good pub guide. A multitude of chamber pots festoons the two heavily beamed bars, along with copper pans, harnesses, gin traps and much more. One room was converted from the stable (the original hay racks can still be seen along one wall), and open fires broadcast cheering warmth throughout. Children over 14 welcome. Garden and ample parking. Spinners Garden (noted for rare shrubs) nearby.

THE NEW FOREST INN

Emery Down, Lyndhurst. Tel. (0703) 282329

Location: Village centre, ½ mile from A35.
Credit cards: Access, Visa.
Accommodation: 4 doubles en suite. £25 single, £50 double, incl.
Bitters: Flowers Original, Strong Country, Wadworth 6X.
Lagers: Stella Artois, Heineken.

Examples of bar meals (lunch & evening, 7 days): *fillet of pork in green peppercorn sauce, breast of chicken in stilton sauce, veal italian, salmon in champagne, pigeon breast Rufus, garlic & herb pasta, steak. Hot apple & cider pudding, homemade cheesecake.*

There's a story that in the early 1700's beer was sold from a caravan on this site, having claimed squatter's rights, and that caravan now forms the front lounge porchway. Stranger still, the sound of curtains drawn on brass rings can apparently be heard daily at 5pm! Three rooms open off the single servery: the lower bar, which seats 18; the main bar, with private 'bays' (including the body of the caravan); and the lighter upper bar, decorated by old farm implements. Morris dancers perform on occasion, and the Hampshire Youth Orchestra give concerts in the garden, which on a long summer evening here in the heart of the New Forest must be a delight. Children are welcome, and will no doubt head for the ponies in the neighbouring paddock. Sue and Nick Emberley are also proprietors of the Trusty Servant at Minstead and the Fleur de Lys at Pilley, and maintain high standards of good, imaginative food at each.

THE TRUSTY SERVANT

Minstead, Lyndhurst.   Tel. (0703) 812137
          Location: On village green, 1 mile off A31.
   Credit cards: Access, Visa.
Accommodation: 3 singles (£25), 4 doubles (£50), all en suite.
          Bitters: Flowers Original, Strong Country, Wadworth 6X.
           Lagers: Heineken, Stella Artois.

Examples of bar meals (lunch & evening, 7 days): *potato & cauliflower soup, Brazilian style beef, beef curry, mixed grill, steak, lamb chops in orange & mint sauce, pasta pepperoni, haddock, fresh crab, ploughman's. Hot chocolate fudge cake, treacle & walnut tart.*
NB New restaurant opening July 1991.

This fine example of a Victorian New Forest Hotel is undergoing refurbishment, with the addition of a new restaurant scheduled for July 1991. A safe garden to the rear is also taking shape, but the front patio (with tables and chairs) enjoys a pleasant aspect over the village green. The name apparently came from a Winchester college, and the inn sign depicts what must be the earliest job description of a trusty servant. Sue and Nick Emberley are the proprietors, who also own the Fleur de Lys at Pilley and New Forest Inn at Emery Down. Sue supervises the cooking herself, and the menu is quite sizeable. They welcome children, who will be attracted to the paddock housing the famous New Forest ponies. A large barn is available for weddings and other functions, and barn dances will be arranged. Conan Doyle is buried in the nearby churchyard.

THE TUDOR ROSE INN

Burgate, Fordingbridge. Tel. (0425) 652227

Location: On A338 1½ miles north of Fordingbridge.
Credit cards: Access, Visa.
Bitters: Wadworth 6X, Ringwood, Bass, Newquay Steam.
Lagers: Fosters, Newquay Steam, Grunhalle.

Examples of bar meals (lunch & evening, except Sun. lunch): *Tudor Rose chicken (tender breast with chef's special sauce), mixed grill, grilled local trout, king prawns, steaks, horseshoe gammon, giant Yorkshire puddings, ploughman's, daily specials.*
Examples of restaurant meals (as above): *potato skins & chilli, combos (eg rump steak, seafood platter, garlic mushrooms, garlic bread, French fries or jacket potato), steaks, chicken Kiev, scampi, plaice, cheeseburger, salads, daily specials.*

If you wonder why there are so few doors inside, then you may prefer not to know that they have been removed due to the ghost of a Cavalier, killed here by Roundheads, who, it is said, would politely knock on doors, only to slam them violently behind him! He haunts one of the most beautiful and best preserved Tudor buildings in England. Any unnatural chill would have been dispelled by the magnificent double breasted 15th century fireplace, and the rich red carpet also lends warmth. The massive beams and supports shake a little to the sounds of live music, plus occasional liveley special evenings. John and Lyn Butler welcome children, and have large gardens (with barbecue) to front and rear (the latter overlooking fields), which is as well in summer, for the inn is very popular locally and with passers by.

THE CARTWHEEL INN

Whitsbury, nr Fordingbridge.   Tel. (0725 3) 362

Location:	Village centre.
Credit cards:	Amex, Diners, Visa, Mastercard, Eurocard.
Bitters:	Examples:- Adnams Broadside, Bass, Flowers Original, Marston's Pedigree, Wadworth 6X, McEwans Export, Worthington, Mitchels Mild.
Lagers:	Examples:- Carlsberg, Fosters, Heineken, Stella Artois.

Examples of bar/restaurant meals (lunch & evening, except Tues evening): *smoked halibut, homecooked steak & kidney pudding, lasagne, chilli, steaks, swordfish steak, scampi, cod, plaice, pizza, cashew paella, pasta parmagiana, salads, ploughman's, sandwiches, daily specials. Chocolate fudge cake, profiteroles, bread pudding.*

"Slightly off the beaten track, but never in a rut!" - this Cartwheel is the only pub for miles around, but that's not why it is so well used by locals, nor why it is rated by major guides. It's a fine example of an unpretentious working village local, serving an exceptional range of beers and good food. The magnificent Desert Orchid ("Dessie") is stabled in Whitsbury - there is some influence from the stud farm, but one could not describe the inn as 'horsey'. It was once a wheelwright's (hence the name), prior to that a bakery, and back in the 1800's a barn. Momentos from its past make interesting decor. Two main bars, a games room (with pool and darts) and dining room are all imbued with warmth and character. Ian and Jeanie are young licensees, but have already put in over six years here. Their garden has play equipment and barbecue, but unfortunately there is no facility for children inside the pub.

THE GEORGE INN

Vernham Dean, nr Andover.   Tel. (0264 87) 279

Location:	Village centre, 3 miles off A343.
Credit cards:	Not accepted.
Bitters:	Marston's.
Lagers:	Marston's Pilsner, Stella Artois.

Examples of bar meals (lunch & evening, 7 days): *George Inn mushrooms (garlic flavoured topped with cheese & bacon), homemade soups, corned beef hash pie, ploughman's, many daily specials eg chicken in white wine, cottage pie, bacon & cheese layer pie, 'leeky rakes', liver & bacon, lasagne.*

Close to the Wiltshire and Berkshire borders in wonderful walking country, this picture-book early 17th century inn is immediately likeable. Perhaps it's the tiled roof curving over the windows, or the fairly uncommon timbered brick and flint walls, but on entering one's first impressions are confirmed. Each of the heavily timbered bars has a fireplace, the main bar an inglenook with seating. Furnishings are simple but comfortable, but most important, perhaps, is the good, wholesome, homecooked food, changing daily, plus the esteemed Marston's ales, which have earned a place in major good pub guides. Mary Perry, an amiable landlady ably assisted by husband Philip, is the force behind this; she has spent 21 years running local pubs, the last two at this one. They have a family room and attractive garden. Well controlled dogs permitted. Car park.

THE CARPENTER'S ARMS

Harts Lane, Burghclere, nr Newbury.   Tel. (0635) 27251

Location:	Village centre, just off A34 3 miles south of Newbury.
Credit cards:	Access, Visa, Eurocard.
Bitters:	Royal Oak, Eldridge Pope, Fullers London Pride, Palmers Best, Hardys Country Ale.
Lagers:	Labatts, Kronenbourg.

Examples from lunchtime menu (7 days): *tiger prawns in chilli & garlic sauce, baked mushrooms with crispy smoked bacon & melted cheddar topping, chicken tikka, moules provencale, strips of spicy steak/chicken, deep fried potato skins with sour cream dip, Caesar salad, ploughman's, sandwiches.*

Examples from evening menu (not Sunday): *many dishes as above, fresh salmon flakes & mussels in saffron sauce with noodles, fillet steak with red wine & port sauce, seafood in provencale sauce. Good desserts.*

Rabbit wasn't on the menu, but then the pub does overlook Watership Down. There are ample alternatives, though, and the stylish and imaginative menus make mouthwatering reading. John and Sheena Evanson have spent the last eight years at this lovely location near the Berkshire border, and have consolidated their success with a new 20-seater restaurant opened only in April '91. Elegantly furnished, it commands the same marvellous view as the garden (with barbecue). The older parts date from the 18th century, and there are tales of a ghost, of which Sheena has direct experience. Certainly there's no trace of a chill in the cosy and comfortable bar. Antique carpentry tools adorn the brick fireplace, and there's an interesting collection of military medals. Children welcome.

THE PELICAN

Silchester Road, Pamber Heath, nr Tadley. Tel. (0734) 700286

Location: Village centre, 1 mile off A340 north of Basingstoke.
Credit cards: Not accepted.
Bitters: Courage Best & Directors, Yorkshire.
Lagers: Fosters, Kronenbourg.

Examples of bar meals (lunch & evening, 7 days): *T-bone, sirloin & fillet steaks, homemade steak pie, lasagne, chilli, minced beef curry, scampi, roast chicken, chicken Kiev, gammon, ploughman's, sandwiches, daily specials eg tandoori pork. Trad. Sun. roasts.*

Ample helpings of good food at reasonable prices are a pretty sure route to popularity (the large car park is a necessity), but the service at this well frequented 17th century pub is never less than efficient and pleasant, courtesy of Dougie and Jacqui Folksman, who've been here 18 months or so. The single bar comprises of three areas, one set aside for dining, and brass and toby jugs adorn the timbers and ceiling. A dartboard provides indoor amusement, while children (who are permitted inside) can vent their energies on a playground in the garden, which also has a barbecue. Nearby Pamber Forest is a nature reserve and site of special scientific interest, and the Roman town of Calleva, the only one in Britain to have been completely excavated, is just two miles away, and has a museum containing many important archaeological finds.

THE CROOKED BILLET

London Road, Hook.   Tel. (0256) 762118

Location: On A30, ½ mile east of Hook.
Credit cards: Not accepted.
Bitters: Wadworth 6X, HSB, Marstons Pedigree, Boddingtons, Courage Best, Courage Directors, guests.
Lagers: Fosters, Kronenbourg, Hofmeister.

Examples of bar meals (lunch & evening, 7 days): *classic combo (deep fried mushrooms, golden scampi, deep fried chicken fillets, with barbecue sauce or garlic butter), all day breakfast, steaks, homemade seafood pasta, curry, chilli, moussaka, vegetable lasagne, jacket potatoes, salads, ploughman's, sandwiches, daily specials. Tennessee grasshopper pie, hot Alabama fudge cake, apple pie, icecreams & sorbets.*

A billet is a piece of wood, designed to tell travellers that here is a place of rest and refreshment. It is indeed singularly restful to sit by a river, and the Whitewater (full of trout) runs through the large, pleasant garden, a quiet refuge from the busy A30. Refreshment comes in the form of an excellent range of beers, and a wide choice of mostly homecooked food, supplemented further on special nights. Richard and Sally Sanders are friendly young hosts; they've been here since September '86, and oversaw full refurbishment in '88. Two log fires and an 'old world' bar belie the true age of the building; it dates from 1934, yet has already managed to accumulate a crop of ghost stories. The spacious eating area is full of nooks and crannies, and nicely furnished and carpeted throughout. Children and dogs on leads are welcome. Ample parking.

THE BARLEY MOW

The Hurst, Winchfield, nr Basingstoke.   Tel. (0256) 617490

Location: Village centre, 1 mile off A30.
Credit cards: Not accepted.
Bitters: Courage Directors & Best, John Smiths.
Lagers: Fosters, Hofmeister, Kronenbourg.

Examples from lunchtime menu (7 days): *homemade chicken curry, macaroni cheese, grilled Wiltshire gammon, steaks, Barley Mow bangers in curry sauce, salads, omelettes, jacket potatoes, ploughman's, sandwiches, daily specials. Trad. Sun. roasts.*
Examples from evening menu (7 days): *tacos, Winchfield grill, steaks, beef Italienne, tagliatelle carbonara, honey roast duck, grilled trout, daily specials.*

Lords has its 'Long Room', but The Barley Mow has its 'Short Room', complete with dart board. The pub stands opposite the village cricket ground, hence the connection. Irony and witty repartee are often to be heard from the locals in the public bar, and proprietors Maurice and Christine Seymour are always on hand with friendly exchanges. Christine does the cooking herself at lunchtimes, which may be savoured in dining room or lounge bar (children permitted only if eating). Both bars are well upholstered, beamed and carpeted, and the lounge has a log fire. The large beer garden has a barbecue, and the reclaimed Basingstoke Canal runs right past. Two large car parks.

THE FOX

Green Lane, Ellisfield, nr Basingstoke.   Tel. (0256) 381210

Location:	3 miles off A339 via B3046, southern edge of village.
Credit cards:	Access, Visa, Mastercard, Eurocard.
Bitters:	Marston's Pedigree, Wadworth 6X, Gales HSB, Bunces, Theakston's Old Peculier.
Lagers:	McEwans, Becks.

Examples of bar meals (lunch & evening, except Mon evening): *casseroles (eg steak & kidney, lamb & orange, beef in beer, venison), extra hot chilli, 20ozs T-bone, peppered sirloin, fillet steaks, salmon, trout, vegetarian dish, jacket potatoes, ploughman's, sandwiches.*

In the lovely rolling countryside of the North Downs, The Fox is about as remote as you can be in Hampshire, yet people travel some distance to seek it out. Word has spread of the very good food and exceptional range of quality ales, not overlooked either by Egon Ronay and Camra guides. Few come only once, most return again and again, for licensees (of three years) Ray and Glenys strive to make sure that their guests always enjoy their visit. One may partake of their homecooked fare in either bar. 16th century in origin, the main lounge is split level, with exposed beams, open fireplace, comfortable seating and an attractive bay window. Darts are played in the public bar, where dogs are permitted. Children are allowed only in the rather nice garden. Car parking.

THE QUEEN INN

Down Street, Dummer, nr Basingstoke.   Tel. (0256) 397367

Location: Village centre, ½ mile from jnctn 7 of M3.
Credit cards: Access, Visa, Amex, Switch.
Bitters: Courage Best, Directors, Wadworth 6X.
Lagers: Kronenbourg, Hofmeister, Fosters.

Examples of bar/restaurant meals (lunch & evening, except Sun evening): *steaks, wholeknuckle of ham roasted with honey, fresh Scotch salmon, whole plaice, deep pan lasagne, moussaka, chilli, duck a l'orange, lemon chicken, salads, daily specials. Homemade cheesecake, chocolate mousse, fruit pie, tipsy trifle. Trad. 4-course Sun. lunch £8.95.*

Royal connections go beyond just the name; the Duchess of York was raised in this village, and she still has family here. The press apparently took over the pub on the announcement of her engagement! An oil painting of her wedding is displayed in the restaurant, and there's also a portrait of her mother-in-law, the queen. However, we lesser mortals are equally assured of a genuine welcome from John and Jocelyn Holland, who've 'reigned' for over seven years. Their well-timbered 17th century pub has just the one, L-shaped bar, warmed by a large open fire, but also has a restaurant area (children welcome) and four other sections where bar food may be consumed. That is except for Sunday evenings, which is set aside for live music. Bar billiards is another entertainment. Patio and car park.

THE PLOUGH INN

East Stratton, nr Winchester.   Tel. (0962 89) 241

Location:	½ mile off A33.
Credit cards:	Not accepted.
Accommodation:	1 double en suite (£45), 3 twins (£38/£40). Tv's, tea & coffee.
Bitters:	Butser Brew, HSB, Ringwood 49.
Lagers:	Carlsberg Hof & Pilsner, Carling.

Examples of bar meals (lunch & evening, Tues - Sun): *beef curry, Gambas prawns in garlic butter, chilli, rumpsteak (evenings only), homemade burgers (evenings only), ploughman's, sandwiches, daily specials eg rabbit casserole. Whisky bread pudding with whisky sauce, rhubarb tart.*
Examples of restaurant meals (evenings Wed - Sun): *homemade soups (noted), braised pigeon, jugged hare, game casserole, steaks, beef in Guinness, fillets of plaice stuffed with seafood, salmon steak. Trad. Sun. lunches.*

Country pursuits are a theme at this 19th century former bakery, in a lovely thatched village (mentioned in Domesday). Those fond of hare, pheasant, partridge et al will find much to please them, but there are plenty of alternatives, all prepared by landlady Trudy Duke, whose soups enjoy a special reputation. Son Richard is the sportsman, and charming old pictures of game birds and country scenes grace the dining room (known as the 'game room') and two bars, both warmed by open fires. The lounge is quiet and restful, the public has darts, and is where the locals gather. A skittle alley doubles as a function room, and there's live music on occasion. Children are welcome, and a tractor is amongst the play equipment on the large green at the front.

THE CART & HORSES INN

London Road, Kingsworthy, nr Winchester. Tel. (0962) 882360

Location: Village centre, just off A34/A33 junction.
Credit cards: Access, Visa.
Bitters: Marstons, Burtons.
Lagers: Stella Artois, Heineken, Marstons, Swan Light.

Examples of bar meals (lunch & evening, 7 days): *fresh crab, homemade curries, seafood platter, lamb & apricot pie, liver & onions, smoked trout, steaks, chilli, scampi, whole lemon sole, pasta vegetable bake, salads, cold buffet. Fresh fruit pie, treacle tart, liqueur chocolate mousse. Children's menu.*
Examples of restaurant meals (every evening, lunchtime carvery only): *escalope of veal Italian style, mixed fish or meats grill, chicken breast with lobster & prawn filling & seafood sauce, steaks, Somerset pork.*

This strikingly pretty 16th century inn draws in many a traveller on the way to the coast or New Forest. Now just off the main road, it once stood on the old drovers' road to Winchester, but the flower cart remains a colourful local landmark. For 22 years David Smith has been the genial host, aided by friendly and efficient staff. Food is of a very high order, and the magnificent buffet bar will set the gastric juices flowing. The two bars and 40 seater restaurant are comfortably accommodated and adorned with brass and hunting horns. There's a family room, and a skittle alley doubles as a function and meeting room - other indoor amusements include bar billiards and darts. Weekend barbecues are popular, to be enjoyed in the sun-trap patio or attractive garden, which has trampolines and swings.

THE BUSH INN

Ovington, nr Alresford.   Tel. (0962) 732764
      Location: In village by river Itchen, ½ mile off A31.
   Credit cards: Visa, Mastercard, Amex.
      Bitters: Wadworth 6X, Flowers, HSB, guests.
      Lagers: Stella Artois, Heineken.

Examples of bar meals (lunch & evening, 7 days): *grilled Itchen trout, homemade chilli, steak & kidney pie, green lipped mussels in garlic butter, scampi, sirloin steak, macaroni cheese, cold fish platter, salads, ploughman's, sandwiches. Children's menu. Homemade fruit pie, meringue & black cherry surprise.*
Examples of restaurant meals (lunch & evening, except Sun evening): *grilled halibut (with prawns, red caviar, cream dill & tomato), lobster (with scallops, prawns, haddock & mushrooms), venison with pear & cranberry sauce, duck with redcurrant & mint sauce, Bush Inn fillet (with stilton & bacon in cream sauce), Bush Pekinese stir fry. Raspberries with walnut shortbread, rich chocolate fondue, crepes jubilee. Trad. Sun. roasts.*

Derived, appropriately, from the Roman word for 'resting place', The Bush stands on the Pilgrim's Way, and has provided rest and refreshment to the weary traveller since the 16th century. And what an idyllic spot to do so, with lovely riverside walks and beautiful shaded garden. The inn itself is a well suited for quiet repose: no juke boxes etc, but fires in every room, old timbers, clocks and furniture, and many brasses, coppers and antiques. Service is friendly and efficient, and the menus are very diverse and imaginative, both in bar and high class restaurant, as the examples above indicate. Robert Middleton and Peter Kelly are your hosts, who welcome children.

THE SILVER BIRCH INN

Greatham, nr Liss.   Tel. (042 07) 262
        Location: Northern edge of village on A325.
    Credit cards: Access, Visa, Mastercard.
Accommodation: 1 single (£25), 3 doubles (£45). Showers, tv's, tea & coff.
        Bitters: Gale's HSB, Yorkshire, Watney's SP.
        Lagers: Holsten, Fosters, Carlsberg. Plus Scrumpy Jack cider.

Examples of bar/restaurant meals (lunch & evening, 7 days): *steaks, chicken with prawns & lobster, pork steaks in fine herbs, Hungarian goulash, curry, duckling a l'orange, plaice filled with prawns & mushrooms, pan fried trout with sage & butter sauce, mushroom & potato pie, courgettes crumble, salads. Trad. Sun. roasts.*

Much more attractive inside than out, this turn-of-the-century inn is distinguished in a number of ways. The main feature of the very spacious lounge bar is a huge stone surround fireplace. A wrought iron doorway leads to the pleasant 32-seater restaurant, with warm velvet drapes. The Barn Bar (the bar itself is actually thatched) has a rural theme, with rustic style seating, and a 90-seater function room would be suitable for weddings etc. But it is the faces behind the bar that count for most, and jovial landlord Ron Hawkin (who cooks) and wife Rita have kept their humour here for over three years. Also well kept are the ales, and the comfortable bedrooms - this is a handy stopping off point on the way to the coast, but is worth a stay on its own merit. Children are welcome and have a play area in the rear garden (with barbecue).

THE CEDARS VILLAGE PUB & RESTAURANT

Binsted, nr Alton.   Tel. (0420) 22112

Location:	Village centre.
Credit cards:	Not accepted.
Accommodation:	2 twins, 2 family, £18.50 - £20.
Bitters:	Courage Directors & Best.
Lagers:	Kronenbourg, Fosters, Hofmeister.

Examples of bar/restaurant meals (lunch & evening, except Tues evening): *clam fries, smoked salmon flutes filled with crab mayonnaise (topped with prawns), goose breast (with ginger, spring onion & gooseberry sauce), Desperate Dan's special steaks, pork marsala, seafood platter, 1½lb Dover sole, rack of lamb, vegetarian dishes (speciality), daily specials. Trad. Sun. roasts plus alternatives £7.95 + 10% service.*

Field Marshall Lord Montgomery lived and was laid to rest in this little village, on the old Pilgrims' Way. In his day there were three pubs here, but now this is the one and only. When Babs and Terry Nye arrived 12 years ago, it was a typical village 'boozer', but they have established a first class restaurant whilst maintaining country pub traditions and locals' loyalty. The ever-changing menus make mouthwatering reading, and vegetables in particular are treated with imagination - Babs was a vegetarian. Definitely not for 'herbivores' are the gigantic steaks, which in part may explain why the Cedars appears in 'The American's guide to England'. Barbecues and special nights are good fun, and there's pool and darts. Children are welcome if eating, and there are swings and sports opposite. Jane Austen's house nearby. Ample parking.

SURREY

near Box Hill.

THE MARINERS HOTEL

Millbridge, Frensham. Tel. (025 12) 4747/2050

Location:	On A287, halfway between Farnham and Hindhead.
Credit cards:	Access, Visa, Mastercard, Eurocard, Amex.
Accommodation:	6 singles, 6 doubles, 8 twins, 1 family. All with full facilities. Special weekend breaks.
Bitters:	Websters, Ruddles, Marston's Pedigree, Royal Oak.
Lagers:	Fosters, Carlsberg, Holsten, Kaliber.

Examples of bar/restaurant meals (lunch & evening, 7 days, all day Sun): *homemade soups, deepfried mushrooms with garlic dip, homemade pizzas, steaks with various sauces, self-serve cold meat buffet & salad bar, daily specials. Children's menu. Homemade gateaux. Trad. Sun. roasts.*

You would barely imagine, admiring the view over the lovely Wey Valley, that the hotel is within an hour of central London, Heathrow or Gatwick. This is one of Surrey's most peaceful and beautiful corners, surrounded by National Trust land and many outdoor activities. Being a family run hotel, pride is taken in the relaxed informality combined with professional service. A fine example of early Victorian architecture, The Mariners is full of character, the timbered bar warmed by log fires, and the opulent restaurant (with dance floor) commanding superb views. Pizzas and pastas are specialities, and the buffet is very popular. Children are welcome, and can play in the garden (with two patios). Quality accommodation and excellent facilities for business meetings/conferences, wedding receptions etc. Live music Monday evenings.

THE SQUIRREL INN

Hurtmore Road, Hurtmore, nr Godalming.   Tel. (0483) 860223

Location:	Just off A3, 5 miles south of Guildford.
Credit cards:	Access, Visa, Diners, Amex.
Accommodation:	3 singles, 5 doubles, 1 twin, all with full facilities.
Bitters:	Ruddles, Websters.
Lagers:	Holsten Export, Carlsberg, Fosters.

Examples of bar meals (lunch & evening, 7 days): *fisherman's pie, spicy chicken satay, grilled Portuguese sardines, Scotch smoked salmon, pie of the day, homemade pasta, omelettes, eggs benedict, filled jacket potatoes, ploughman's, sandwiches, daily specials.* Examples of restaurant meals (as above): *'sizzlers from the stone', king scallops, lobster tails, surf & turf, chicken tandoori, minted lamb, curry, chilli, daily specials eg grilled trout with lemon & capers. Treacle tart, fruit crumble, steamed puddings.*

Though only 50 yards from the busy A3, this friendly 17th century inn remains a peaceful refuge behind the contours of the land. Although an ideal refreshment stop on the way to or from Portsmouth, under the stewardship of David and Jane Barnes it has acquired firm local support, and recommendations from major guides. The airy interior comprises two dining rooms (one for non-smokers), a conservatory, and a panelled lounge with comfortable settees, decorated with china plates, tasteful pictures and stuffed animals. Children have their own room and are safe in the garden. Menus are extensive and varied, yet all is homecooked - you may even like to cook-your-own, on the hot stones brought to the table! Large car park.

THE CROWN INN

Chiddingfold.   Tel. (0428 79) 2255/6
              Location: On A283.
          Credit cards: Access, Visa, Diners, Amex.
        Accommodation: 1 single, 5 doubles, 2 twins, all with full facilities.
                           3 rooms have 4-posters.
               Bitters: Badger, Tanglefoot, guests.
                Lagers: Hofbrau, guests.

Examples of bar meals (lunch & evening, 7 days): *beef rissoles, steak & kidney pie, spicy chicken, mixed seafood crepes, hot & sour veg & nuts.*
Examples of restaurant meals (lunch & evening except Mons): *feuillette of asparagus & broccoli, fillet of salmon trout on watercress & lime fondue, fillet steak with oysters, breast of chicken stuffed with prawns & cooked in lobster & vermouth sauce, chateaubriand. Trad. Sun. roasts.*

One of the finest examples of a medieval (1258) timber building in the country, The Crown inspires awe in visitors from the New World. They step inside to be confronted by superb linenfold panelling, leaded glass windows, ornate ceilings and enormous fireplaces - fit for royalty, including Edward VI and Elizabeth I who stayed here. Coins dating from the latter's reign were found during building work some years ago. In such surrounds it is almost as a bonus that the food is also first class, whether a la carte in the restaurant or buffet style in the Huntsman Bar. A marvellous venue for a wedding reception, and also to stay, being close to London etc, yet in lovely countryside. Children welcome. Barbecues in small garden Sunday lunchtimes in summer.

THE PLOUGH INN

Coldharbour, nr Dorking. Tel. (0306) 711793

Location: Village centre.
Credit cards: Not accepted.
Accommodation: 1 double, 1 twin. £37.50 per room, B & B.
Bitters: Theakstons Old Peculier, Old Thumper, Bishop's Tipple, Adnams Broadside, guests.
Lagers: Carlsberg, Carlsberg Export, Stella Artois.

Examples of bar/restaurant meals (lunch & evening, 7 days): *homemade steak & kidney pie, chicken & leek pie, shepherds pie, fisherman's pie, braised steak in Guinness with dumplings, scampi classico, toad-in-the-hole, mixed grill, steaks, stuffed salmon trout, jacket potatoes. Old fashioned English puddings. Trad. Sun. roasts.*

At almost 1,000 ft, this is the highest pub in the south east of England, so is looked up to in every sense. On a clear day the views, over 13 counties, are quite stunning - one can even count tower blocks in faraway London. If this were not reason enough for a visit, the inn itself is in the top rank, highly rated by national good pub guides. Good, wholesome English cooking (and beer) is the forte, on an everchanging menu which may be sampled in either of the two bars or 30-seater restaurant. Being over 300 years old there is ofcourse a ghost story, but in this case proprietors Richard and Anna Abrehart say they have first hand experience, confirming a village legend. Occasionally a duo plays live music, and there's a pool table and dart board. The garden has a pond and waterfall. Family room. Great place to stay, near NT Leith Hill.

THE PRINCE OF WALES

Shere, nr Guildford.　　　　　　　　　　　　　　　Tel. (048 641) 2313

　　　　Location:　Just beyond village square, ½ mile off A25.
　Credit cards:　Not accepted.
　　　　　Bitters:　Youngs Ordinary, Special, Extra Light LA.
　　　　　Lagers:　Youngs London & Premium, Castlemaine, Labatts.

Examples of bar meals (every lunchtime, evenings Wed - Sat, plus Sundays in summer): *fresh local trout, homemade steak & kidney pie, chicken & mushroom pie, curries, scampi, plaice, cod, vegetarian lasagne, salads, ploughman's, sandwiches, daily specials. Banana split, apple pie.*

"The most beautiful village in Surrey" - an assertion commonly heard but rarely disputed. The river Tillingbourne (famed for trout) glides through the heart of Shere, wonderfully peaceful except for the raucous squabbling of ducks, themselves an attraction. This idyll would be incomplete without the friendly local, and the 19th century Prince of Wales amply fulfills the role. Landlord Bob Lintill, who's been here 12 years, is a mine of information about the locale, and will readily tell a few tales, including that of the legend of the 'silent pool'. Wife Kathy prepares generous portions of good food at reasonable prices. Sunday evening in winter is quiz night, and there's occasional live entertainment, but darts, pool and crib are always to hand. Children and dogs are welcome, and there's a garden with barbecue.

THE BLACK SWAN

Old Lane, Ockham, nr Cobham.   Tel. (0932) 862364

Location: 1½ miles north of Ockham.
Credit cards: Access, Visa.
Bitters: London Pride, ESB, Theakston's Old Peculier, Tanglefoot, Ruddles Best, many guests.
Lagers: Stella Artois, Fosters, Holsten, Carlsberg.

Examples of bar/restaurant meals (lunchtime & evening, except Sun & Mon evening): *chargrill steaks, honey roast duck a l'orange, scampi bonne femme, grilled Dover sole, chicken Kiev, burgers, spaghetti gamberetti, daily specials. Trad. Sun. roasts.*

An astonishing choice of 14 real ales makes this 17th century pub something of a Mecca for beer drinkers, but it is also well suited to families, out for the day in summer. Not only is there are a large garden (with barbecue), but also a playground and adjoining field, plus a games room inside for not-so-sunny days. Whatever the season, the elegant 50-seater 'Cygnet' restaurant (available for functions) serves quality food, attended by owner Denis Read and his amiable staff. This may also be enjoyed in the bars, one of which has pool and darts, both having exposed beams, comfortable seating and fireplace. Youngsters are drawn to the twice weekly disco, and there's a live band one Monday in each month. Dogs permitted. Ample parking. Wisley Gardens nearby.

THE CRICKETERS

Downside, Cobham.   Tel. (0932) 862105

Location: 2 miles south of Cobham on East Horsley road.
Credit cards: Access, Visa, Diners, Amex, Grand Met.
Bitters: Ruddles County & Best, Websters.
Lagers: Carlsberg, Fosters, Holsten, Budweiser.

Examples of bar meals (lunch & evening, 7 days): *buffet bar & salads, variety of raised pies, chicken a la creme, gammon, trout, lamb chop, veal masala, daily specials.*
Examples of restaurant meals (lunch & evening, Tues - Sun lunch): *mango & prawn with coronation sauce, deep fried lymeswold cheese with plum sauce, escalope of veal princess, devilled rack of lamb, tournedos nicoise, Caribbean Dover sole (with lobster & sauce), almond & vegetable risotto. Trad. Sun. roasts.*

If you hadn't planned to eat, a glimpse of the buffet bar, arrayed with a wide range of salads and raised pies, is likely to change your mind. Alternatively, the table d'hote menu, very popular with business people, offers a choice of good, hot traditional food. Indeed, this is a place where the best traditions of the English country inn are well observed; standing on the village common, and with a lovely garden, the fact that it is over 300 years old is evident from the wattle and daub walls, still visible in parts. Low beamed ceilings, beautiful brickwork, open fireplace and cosy alcoves all make their contribution, but Brian and Wendy Luxford and staff create the friendly atmosphere. Children are allowed in the Stable Bar, there's also a separate restaurant with exceptionally good wine list, and all just 10 minutes from junction 10 of the M25!

THE WOODCOCK INN

Woodcock Hill, Felbridge.   Tel. (0342) 325859

Location:	North of village on A22.
Credit cards:	Access, Visa.
Accommodation:	2 doubles (£35), 2 suites (£55 & £65). TV's, 'phones, breakfast in rooms. Special rates on request.
Bitters:	Larkins, Gibbs New, Exmoor, Harveys Armada, Ringwood.
Lagers:	Fosters, Holsten Export.

Examples of bar meals (lunch & evening, 7 days): *wild duck in red wine, chicken Kiev, moussaka, steaks, mixed shellfish, ploughman's, sandwiches, daily specials, cold buffet in summer.*

Examples of restaurant meals (as above - booking advised weekends): *selection of fresh fish (displayed), hot croissant filled with shellfish, game in season, maigret of duck, calves liver grilled with bacon & sage, lobster, chef's specials, extensive choice for Sun. lunch.*

"Good food is an art", says landlady Valerie Jones on her menu - her creations have won very high ratings for her characterful 15th century inn in a leading national good pub guide. Flexibility is a key word; everyone is treated as an individual, and menus tailored to suit. Fresh fish is the forte, including some quite uncommon, such as pike. Also very uncommon are the furnishings; upholstered milk churns as bar stools, lacquered oriental benches, fancy fans and parasols are amongst a host of collectables and antiques. A black spiral staircase leads to a candlelit gallery and function room for 100, and on to a Victorian style dining room, bookable for private parties up to 18. Children are welcome, and there is a patio.

THE HAYCUTTER

Tanhouse Road, Broadham Green, nr Oxted.   Tel. (0883) 712550

Location: On village green, south of old Oxted.
Credit cards: Not accepted.
Bitters: Friary Meux, John Bull, Youngs, Tetley, Burton.
Lagers: Lowenbrau, Skol, Castlemaine.

Examples of bar/restaurant meals (lunch & evening, Mon - Sat): *lobster bisque, scallops provencale, avocado & chicken salad, dressed crab salad, plaice stuffed with prawns & mushrooms, veal cordon bleu, lamb chops, grilled sardines, fresh fish, steaks, ploughman's, sandwiches, daily specials. Complimentary bar nibbles on Sundays. Fresh desserts.*

Catering is a demanding profession (imagine throwing a dinner party for umpteen guests, 12 times per week); an unforgiving public remembers only the last meal, and if it was not up to expectations one stands condemned for ever. So it is sheer consistency that is the keynote of this successful country pub, quietly situated by the village green. All is fresh and cooked to order, and always of a high standard - fish and steaks are especially noted - and accompanied by a good wine list. One may dine in the single bar or separate restaurant (children welcome), amidst the old beams and an unusual collection of regimental hats. A skittles alley can be reserved for parties and meetings, with food laid on, and barbecues are arranged occasionally in season in the large garden. Barry Aldridge, daughter Sheelagh and staff are on hand with a cordial greeting. Ample parking.

THE BELL INN

Outwood Lane, Outwood, nr Redhill.   Tel. (0342) 842989/844427
> Location: Next to windmill on Smallfield to Bletchingly road.
> Credit cards: Access, Visa, Amex, Mastercard.
> Bitters: Harveys, Pilgrim, 4 guests.
> Lagers: Heineken, Heineken Export, Carling, Tennants Extra, Stella Artois, McEwans LA.

Examples of bar meals (lunch & evening, 7 days): *indoor barbecue, fillet steak with snails, chicken en croute, beef Bellington, spare ribs, steak & kidney pie, Guinness pie, plaice filled with crab & fresh prawns, roast supreme of duck poached in blackberries & apple kaffif, veg curry/lasagne. Trad. Sun. roasts.*

"Always worth a call" is the pub motto, and indeed it's probably best to call ahead if you want to reserve a table, for this is a very well frequented establishment, used by the many "celebrities" who live in this salubrious area. Built in the 17th century of ships timbers, it has a single L-shaped bar with indoor barbecue, and there's also a barbecue in the beer garden, which straddles a public footpath leading into the heart of Surrey. Any of the paintings for sale in the bar might make a suitable gift. There's always a friendly atmosphere, especially when the log fire is on the go. Of further interest is the duckpond and windmill nearby (the oldest working mill in England). Star rating in leading good pub guide.

THE THAMES COURT

Shepperton Lock, The Towpath, Shepperton.   Tel. (0932) 221957

    Location: From Church Square take Chertsey road, left into Ferry Lane.
Credit cards: Access, Visa, Amex.
     Bitters: Bass, IPA, Wadworth 6X, Fullers London Pride.
     Lagers: Carling, Tennants, Tennants Extra, Warsteiner.

Examples of bar/restaurant meals (12 to 8.30pm daily. Afternoon teas 3.30 to 5.30pm): *steak & kidney pie, shepherds pie, Mexican chicken, beef stroganoff, coq au vin, lasagne, honeybaked gammon, roast duck, fresh poached salmon, carvery, jacket potatoes, vegetarian dishes, daily specials. Cold buffet. Trad. Sun. roasts.*

The Dutch ambassador was once the fortunate occupier of this handsome waterside pub, subsequently an exclusive club. It still looks every inch suited to be the home of an ambassador, beautifully constructed and furnished, and in a marvellous position on the Thames next to busy Shepperton Lock (once classed as Middlesex, but now in Surrey). The main bar is oak panelled and beamed, with a staircase leading to a gallery fitted out in high back seating and private alcoves. The restaurant area (ideal for wedding receptions etc) enjoys lovely views over the water. Food is served buffet style so there is not a long wait, even when busy – which it usually is, especially on summer days and evenings. Fortunately, the garden is large (and has a marquee). Children have rooms set aside away from the bar. Peter Langrish-Smith is your host. Ample parking.

THE SURREY CRICKETERS

52 Chertsey Road, Windlesham.   Tel. (0276) 72192

Location: Village centre.
Credit cards: Access, Visa, Diners, Amex.
Bitters: Gales HSB, King & Barnes, Friary Meux, Burton, Tetley.
Lagers: Lowenbrau, Castlemaine, Skol, Swan Light.

Examples of bar meals (11am - 9:30pm, 7 days): *chicken escalope, fillet of plaice, whitebait, lasagne, rump steak, jacket potatoes, variety of ploughman's, good selection of sandwiches & rolls.*
Examples of restaurant meals (every evening): *avocado & crab mousse, mixed veg. terrine, surf & turf, rack of lamb, fillet steak in green peppercorn sauce, supreme of chicken Madagascar, grilled Dover sole, skate wings, scampi provencale. Trad. Sun. roasts.*

The sandwich, like cricket, is a very English invention not always practised as it should be. You will not find tired, curled up cheese at The Cricketers, but rather avocado and crab, smoked salmon or other delicious fillings. The quality of all the food is not in doubt, the choice is wide, and it is available in the bar most of the day. Recent refurbishment has created a most pleasant, airy atmosphere in which to enjoy it. A large open fire divides the timbered bar, where the many brass ornaments include hunting horns and bugles. The elegant restaurant overlooks the garden, and seats 40 in comfort. Arriving only in summer 1990, John and Margaret Nelson are an agreeable couple who have worked hard for their success. They welcome children, and have a large car park. Handy for Ascot and Windsor.

THE WHEATSHEAF

42 Guildford Road, West End, Woking. Tel. (0276) 858652

Location: On A322, 2 miles from junction 3 of M3.
Credit cards: Not accepted.
Bitters: Courage Directors & Best, Wadworth 6X, John Smiths.
Lagers: Fosters, Hofmeister, Kronenbourg, Carlton LA.

Examples of from lunchtime menu (7 days): *rump steak, scampi, plaice, chicken Kiev, omelettes, jacket potatoes, sandwiches, daily specials. Trad. Sun. roasts in winter. Evening (Tues - Sat): steaks, mixed grill, gammon, salads. Treacle sponge, apricot crumble, profiteroles.*

A handily placed watering hole, this, just five minutes from the M3, and a favourite halt for those on the way to or from Ascot, Windsor or the south. The next village is Bisley, only a mile away, and famed for its rifle shooting connections. The single, L-shaped bar lends itself to two distinct moods: one area, the smaller, is quiet and 'intimate', while the larger is livelier and more social. There's also a separate 30-seater dining room and a children's room, but one may eat anywhere. Not uncommon for the early 19th century, the walls are panelled, and adorned with brasses and china plates, as are some of the exposed timbers. French windows lead out to a lovely well-kept garden with wooden benches and tables, and a play area. For over eight years, Larry and Glenys Carty have sustained a friendly welcome (which extends to our canine friends), and prided themselves on offering good value food. Ample parking.

Guildhall, Guildford.

THE JOLLY FARMER

Guildford Road, Runfold, nr Farnham.   Tel. (025 18) 2074
        Location: On A31 (Hog's Back).
    Credit Cards: Access, Visa.
         Bitters: Courage Best & Directors, John Smiths, guest ale.
          Lagers: Kronenbourg, Fosters, Hofmeister, Miller Lite, Carlton LA.

Examples from lunchtime menu (7 days): *clam fries, Jolly Farmer smokies, kipper fillet, scampi, lasagne, nut cutlet, spicy veg burger, jacket potatoes, sandwiches, cold buffet, self-serve salad. Trad. Sun. roasts.*
Evening menu: *lemon sole in mushroom & prawn sauce, mussels in wine & garlic, supreme of chicken Leicestershire filled with stilton & leeks, curry of the day, steaks, vegetable curry/lasagne, salads.*

The Farmer's Table lunchtime buffet (Mon - Sat) would revive the most jaded appetite, and is very popular amongst business people. Families are always welcome, and come especially for the well reputed traditional Sunday lunch (barbecues are also arranged, weather permitting), and children (who eat at special prices) have a climbing frame and house in the garden. From here there are pleasing views over a lake, and being on the famous 'Hog's Back' the pub enjoys a wonderful panorama over Surrey, Hampshire and Berkshire. Of particular note in the large, accommodating interior are the rough hewn elm tables and chairs, and an unusual cornice around the bar, painted in decorative vine leaves. Peter Rainger, landlord since April '91, likes to celebrate national days, so remember St George on April 23rd!

NOTES

NOTES

NOTES

Hampshire, Surrey and West Sussex

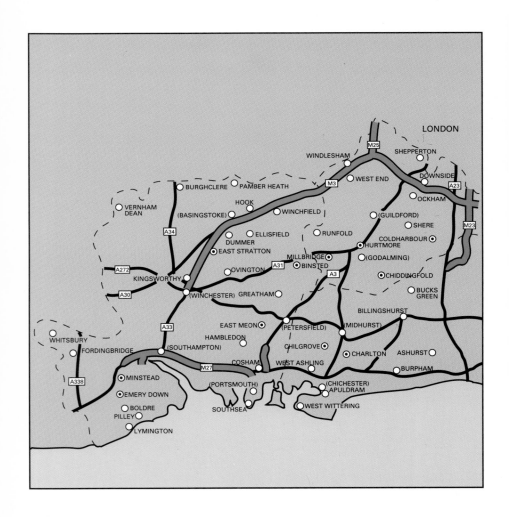

Towns bracketed are not featured in guide.

⊙ accommodation

LOCATOR MAP

Surrey, West Sussex, East Sussex and Kent

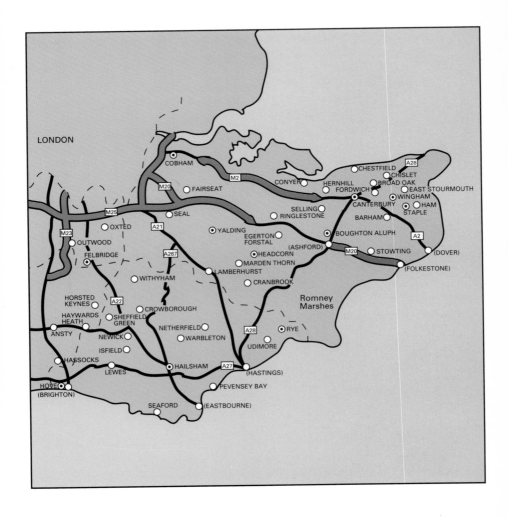

Towns bracketed are not featured in guide.

⊙ accommodation

INDEX

Hampshire

Kent

* accommodation

INDEX

* accommodation

INDEX

Sussex

* accommodation